Electron Microscopy
of Enzymes
Principles and Methods

Electron Microscopy of Enzymes

Principles and Methods

VOLUME 2

Edited by

M. A. HAYAT

Department of Biology
Kean College of New Jersey
Union, New Jersey

VNR VAN NOSTRAND REINHOLD COMPANY
New York   Cincinnati   Toronto   London   Melbourne

Van Nostrand Reinhold Company Regional Offices:
New York   Cincinnati   Chicago   Millbrae   Dallas

Van Nostrand Reinhold Company International Offices:
London   Toronto   Melbourne

Published by Van Nostrand Reinhold Company
450 West 33rd Street, New York, N.Y. 10001

Published simultaneously in Canada by Van Nostrand Reinhold Ltd.

15 14 13 12 11 10 9 8 7 6 5 4 3 2 1

Library of Congress Cataloging in Publication Data

Hayat, M   A
    Electron microscopy of enzymes.

    Includes bibliographies.
    1. Enzymes.   2. Electron microscope—Technique.
I. Title. [DNLM: 1. Enzymes.   2. Microscopy,
Electron.   QU135 H415e 1973]
QP601.H344   574.1'925'028   73-4844
ISBN 0-442-25679-5 (v.2.)

It is a pleasure to dedicate this volume to

Alex B. Novikoff and Arnold M. Seligman

Preface

This is the second volume in the series on the principles and methods employed for studying enzymatic activity. It is encouraging to know that the first volume has been favorably accepted. This volume has developed, over the years, through the joint effort of ten distinguished author-scientists. The book contains new viewpoints with particular regard for current problems.

It is my impression that this volume will fulfill its purpose: to provide an understanding of the usefulness, limitations, and potential of the preparatory procedures used for studying enzymatic activity. I hope that it may prove to arouse more interest in the importance and problems of electron cytochemistry, and to motivate a deeper and refined study of enzymatic activity.

It is a pleasure to acknowledge the cooperation shown by Mrs. Alberta Gordon of Van Nostrand Reinhold Company.

M. A. HAYAT

Contents

2 ACYLTRANSFERASES
Joan A. Higgins

3 POLYPHENOLOXIDASES (PLANTS)
Yvette Czaninski
Anne-Marie Catesson

4 TYROSINASE
John J. Eppig, Jr.

5 SULFATASES
Väinö K. Hopsu-Havu
Heikki Helminen

6 ADENYLATE CYCLASE
Roger C. Wagner
Mark W. Bitensky

7 LIPASE
Tetsuji Nagata

Contents of

Contributors to This Volume

Mark W. Bitensky

Joan A. Higgins

John J. Eppig, Jr.

Väinö K. Hopsu-Havu

Edward Essner

Tetsuji Nagata

Heikki J. Helminen

Roger C. Wagner

Electron Microscopy
of Enzymes
Principles and Methods

1

Hemoproteins

EDWARD ESSNER

Sloan-Kettering Institute for Cancer Research
New York, New York

INTRODUCTION

The application of histochemical methods to the study of hemoproteins was initiated at the turn of the century when Fischel (1910) introduced benzidine as a substrate and demonstrated a thermolabile peroxidase activity in the granules of eosinophilic and neutrophilic leukocytes. The procedure was subsequently modified by Graham (1918), who also suggested the use of α-naphthol. In later studies, additional substrates were proposed as indicators in peroxide-peroxidase systems (Pearse, 1961). These include orthophenylenediamine, the so-called leuko dyes, and 3-amino-9-ethyl-carbazole (Graham *et al.*, 1965), introduced originally by Burstone (1960) for the demonstration of cytochrome oxidase and aminopeptidase activities. Additional references to the earlier literature may be found in the review by Agner (1941). Despite the availability of these and other compounds, benzidine has proved to be the substrate of choice for the light microscopic demonstration of hemoproteins. However, neither benzidine nor the other substrates mentioned above are useful for electron cytochemistry.

The localization of peroxidase activity at the ultrastructural level with benzidine as substrate was first reported by Mitsui (1960), who demonstrated reaction product in the granules of salamander leukocytes. However, the deposits obtained after incubation in benzidine media are generally of irregular size and shape, and have relatively low electron opacity (Mitsui, 1960; Graham and Karnovsky, 1966a; Goldfischer and Essner, 1969). This may necessitate densitometry (Mitsui, 1960) to confirm the reaction or inordinately long incubations to accumulate sufficient end product. For these reasons, the benzidine procedure has not been extensively used for the electron microscopic study of peroxidase or other hemoproteins.

Several substituted benzidines such as o-tolidine, 2,4-diaminofluorene and 2,7-diaminobenzidine have been suggested (Ornstein, 1968). These substrates yield oxidation products that couple rapidly with α-naphthol, forming extremely insoluble precipitates. Apparently, however, they have not yet been tested at the ultrastructural level.

Interest in the study of hemoproteins was revived when Graham and Karnovsky (1966a) introduced 3,3'-diaminobenzidine (DAB) (Fig. 1–1) and demonstrated its usefulness for the ultrastructural localization of peroxidase activity. Oxidized DAB is readily visualized by both light and electron microscopy. These authors also noted that o-dianisidine can be substituted for DAB, but that the end product lacks sufficient electron density.

The DAB procedure or one of its subsequent modifications has since been applied extensively to the localization of hemoproteins in various cells and tissues. Reaction product has been localized in structures such as endoplasmic reticulum, nuclear envelope (Fig. 1–2), Golgi saccules, and various types of granules. It has also been visualized in smaller cytoplasmic components such as pinocytosis vesicles (Fig. 1–6) and ribosomes (see discussion below). These observations are indicative of the high resolution that can be achieved with the DAB procedures. This is due in large measure to the unique properties of oxidized DAB, which may be summarized as follows: finely granular or amorphous form; insolubility in dehydration and embedding agents; high opacity due to formation of insoluble, polymeric complexes with osmium (Fig. 1–1) (Hanker et al., 1967; Seligman et al., 1968); and minimal diffusion under the usual conditions of incubation (however, see below, "Diffusion Artifacts").

Almost all hemoproteins containing an iron porphyrin prosthetic group display peroxidase or peroxidatic activity, and are therefore potentially demonstrable with the DAB procedures. These include the protoheme peroxidases, catalase, the nonenzyme hemoproteins such as hemoglobin, myoglobin, and cytochrome c, and certain heme-containing proteins found in lysosomes and related organelles. Not included in this list are the flavoprotein peroxidases, which contain flavin adenine dinucleotide as prosthetic

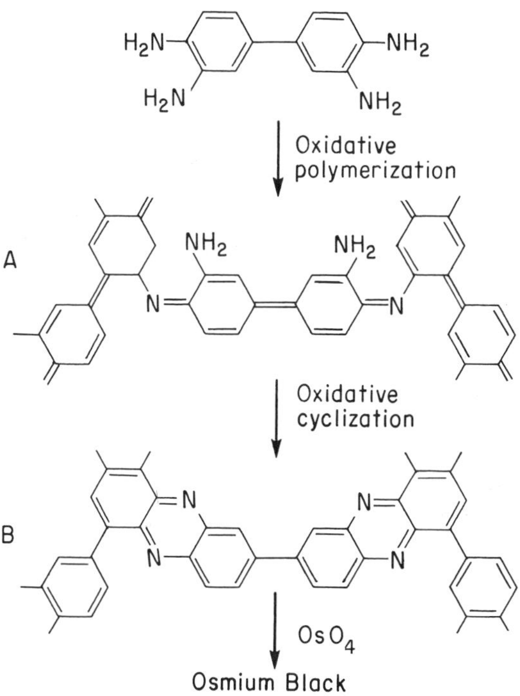

Fig. 1–1. Hypothetical formulation of the oxidative polymerization of DAB to an indamine polymer (A). This may be followed by further quinoid addition to the primary amine resulting in oxidative cyclization to a phenazine polymer (B). A. M. Seligman *et al., J. Cell Biol.* **38**, 1 (1968).

group and lack hematin or metals in significant amounts. For example, glutathione peroxidase found in liver, blood, and other tissues is insensitive to cyanide and azide (Paul, 1963); it does not oxidize *p*-tolidine or guaiacol, and would therefore probably not oxidize DAB. However, such enzymes might be demonstrated by applying the methods recently developed by Hanker *et al.* (1972a and b). These authors have shown that certain transition metal compounds (e.g., cupric ferrocyanide) are capable of catalyzing the nonenzymatic oxidative polymerization of DAB to an indamine-type osmiophilic polymer, and that this principle can be exploited cytochemically for the demonstration of hydrolases and dehydrogenases.

Seligman and colleagues have studied two compounds chemically related to DAB which are oxidized in certain tissues. These are N,N′-bis (4-amino-phenyl)-1,3-xylylenediamine (BAXD) and N,N′-bis (4-amino-phenyl)-N,N′ dimethyl ethylenediamine (BED) (Seligman *et al.,* 1970; Nir and Seligman, 1971). Both compounds are oxidized by horseradish

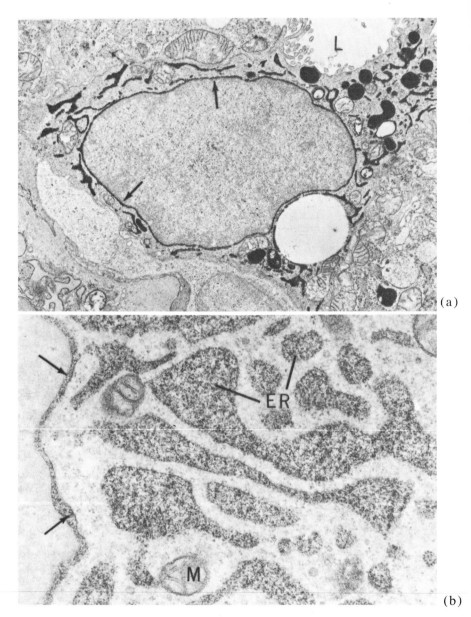

Fig. 1–2a. Intercalated duct cell in rat exorbital lacrimal gland. Fixed in 3% glutaraldehyde for 3 hr; incubated 45 min in DAB medium, pH 7.4, 37°C (Fahimi, 1970). Peroxidase reaction product is localized to endoplasmic reticulum, nuclear envelope (arrows), and various granules. Part of duct lumen (L) is seen. ×12,000.

peroxidase and potassium ferricyanide to an insoluble osmiophilic polymer in a manner analogous to DAB. The oxidations of BAXD and BED will be discussed later in relation to localization in endoplasmic reticulum and mitochondria.

DIAMINOBENZIDINE-PEROXIDASE PROCEDURE

The initial steps involved in preparing tissues for incubation have been outlined elsewhere (Essner, 1973; Hayat, 1973). The dehydration and embedding procedures have been presented by Hayat (1970 and 1972). The same procedure may be used for demonstrating peroxidase activities. The original DAB medium is indicated below together with the appropriate controls.

Graham and Karnovsky's DAB medium (Graham and Karnovsky, 1966a)

3,3'-diaminobenzidine tetra HCl (Sigma)*	5 mg
0.05 M Tris-HCl buffer, pH 7.6	10 ml
1% hydrogen peroxide (freshly prepared from 30% stock, Superoxol, Merck)	0.1 ml

It should be noted that, in general, DAB penetrates tissues relatively slowly. The rate of penetration varies in different tissues. Thus, staining reactions may be absent or much reduced in the deeper portions of the tissues. This applies to small blocks (Brökelmann and Fawcett, 1969) as well as to sections prepared on a tissue sectioner. For instance, Herzog and Miller (1972) have shown that in chopped sections of lacrimal gland incubated for 2 hr in DAB medium, the peroxidase reaction is positive only in a zone extending 20 μ into the tissue from the surface. Therefore, in general, the sections should not exceed 40 μ in thickness. In addition, it is advisable to presoak the sections in a buffered DAB solution without hydrogen peroxide at 4°C from one to several hours to ensure more uniform penetration and staining.

* Since DAB may be carcinogenic and the powder scatters readily, owing to the accumulation of excessive electrostatic charge, it should be handled with appropriate safety equipment (Hanker et al., 1972b).

Fig. 1–2b. Rat intraorbital lacrimal gland. Fixed in 3% glutaraldehyde for 3 hr. Incubated for 90 min in DAB medium, pH 7.4, 37°C (Fahimi, 1970). Portion of acinar cell showing finely granular reaction product in cisternae of endoplasmic reticulum (*ER*) and nuclear envelope (arrows). Mitochondria (*M*) are unstained. ×30,000.

Controls are the following: Complete medium without DAB; complete medium without hydrogen peroxide; complete medium and KCN (10^{-1} to 10^{-3}), complete medium containing 1 to 2% hydrogen peroxide; boil sections for 15 min at 90°C prior to incubation.

Elimination of Endogenous Hydrogen Peroxide

The peroxidatic activity of hemoproteins may persist despite the use of peroxide-free media. This is apparently due to the production of peroxide by tissue oxidase systems. The following controls, which are also applicable to plant tissues (Vigil, 1970), are suggested as a means of eliminating peroxide.

Incubate in hydrogen peroxide-free medium containing beef liver catalase (0.05 to 0.1%; Sigma) (Fahimi, 1968; Cotran and Litt, 1970) or sodium pyruvate (2×10^{-3} M) (Venkatachalam and Fahimi, 1969). It should be noted that catalase may not penetrate appreciably into tissue blocks or chopped sections. Nevertheless, it appears to be useful in preventing the accumulation of hydrogen peroxide in the medium (Seligman et al., 1968). According to Fahimi (1969), pyruvate acts by suppressing the generation of hydrogen peroxide by tissue oxidase systems. However, this may not be the complete explanation, since in at least two instances DAB oxidations have been shown to persist when tissues were incubated under anaerobic conditions. For instance, Frederick and Newcomb (1969) have noted that the oxidation of DAB by leaf peroxisomes is noticeably lessened, but apparently not eliminated, when the reaction is carried out anaerobically without added hydrogen peroxide. In addition, Roels (1970) has reported that incubation of eggs of *Artemia,* under conditions that completely blocked cytochrome oxidase activity, had no effect on the oxidation of DAB in peroxisomes and Golgi cisternae.

Assessing Nonspecific Adsorption of DAB

Incubate in hydrogen peroxide-free medium containing 0.1% catalase; rinse several times in buffer; and incubate in buffer containing potassium ferricyanide (3×10^{-3} M). This compound readily oxidizes DAB (Graham and Karnovsky, 1966a).

Assessing Nonspecific Adsorption of Oxidized DAB

Renew with fresh medium at hourly intervals. Incubate in medium containing oxidized DAB prepared according to Hirai (1968, 1971) or by addition of horseradish peroxidase (0.5 mg/ml) to a solution of DAB (Cotran and Karnovsky, 1968).

Diffusion Artifacts

A freshly prepared solution of DAB is straw-colored, but turns progressively darker, as a result of autooxidation, when allowed to stand at room temperature. Hirai (1968, 1971) has shown that exposure of DAB to oxygen or ultraviolet light promotes autooxidation through condensation of an intermediate (tetraaminobiphenyl oxide) and formation of a partially oxidized end product (DAB oxide). DAB oxide displays affinity for the active site of various hemoproteins, forming spectrophotometrically distinguishable complexes in peroxide-free-media with such proteins as cytochrome c, catalase, and hemoglobin.

In sections of tissues fixed for long periods in glutaraldehyde, DAB oxide can become adsorbed to organelles such as mitochondria and peroxisomes (Hirai, 1971). The latter organelle is discussed in a subsequent section. The mitochondrial reaction is inhibited by potassium cyanide (KCN) and sodium azide (NaN_3), but not by sodium fluoride (NaF), suggesting that the active sites, presumably in the cytochromes of the membranes, remain intact. The staining of peroxisomes, which is blocked by the inhibitor, 3-amino-1,2,4-triazole (AT) (see below, "Catalase"), apparently reflects binding of DAB oxide to catalase, which is present in relatively high concentration in this organelle.

In view of these results, incubation in DAB media should be accompanied by controls of the type indicated above, in order to assess the degree of binding of DAB oxide. It should be noted, however, that relatively little autooxidation occurs in media exposed to air for less than 1 hr. When longer incubations are required, the medium should be renewed at hourly intervals to avoid excessive accumulation of the oxide.

Another, more serious type of artifact is that which results from the diffusion of DAB reaction product (oxidized DAB) from the site of oxidation to structures lacking intrinsic DAB oxidizing activity. This kind of artifact is generally observed in structures that lie in proximity to sites bearing heavy accumulations of reaction product and apparently can occur under the conditions of incubation frequently employed in DAB cytochemistry (Novikoff et al., 1972 b). The recognition that oxidized DAB may diffuse from one structure to another has complicated the interpretation of localizations in mitochondria (see, "DAB Oxidation in Mitochondria") and has raised questions about the localization of catalase or other heme proteins in ribosomes (Goldfischer and Schiller, 1971; Novikoff et al., 1972 b). Ribosomal staining with DAB media has been reported by many investigators in both animal and plant cells (Poux, 1969; Strum and Karnovsky, 1970 b; Legg and Wood, 1970; Wood and Legg, 1970; Rigatsu et al., 1970; Czaninsky and Catesson, 1970; Fahimi, 1971; Goldfischer and Schiller, 1971; Dvorak et al., 1972). Several authors have interpreted ribosomal staining in hepatocytes as indicating the synthesis or site of activation of catalase. For instance, in rats injected with the hypolipidemic agent, Clofibrate, Legg and Wood (1970) observed that membrane-bound ribosomes that were adjacent to reactive peroxisomes were stained following incubation in DAB medium (see also Wood and Legg, 1970). These results were interpreted as evidence that catalase was synthesized on ribosomes of the rough endoplasmic reticulum and was then transferred directly into peroxisomes without traversing the endoplasmic reticulum. Similarly, ribosomal staining was noted by Fahimi (1971) in preliminary studies of rat liver during regeneration or following administration of Clofibrate. He reported that "catalase" reaction product was localized to free and bound ribosomes at the periphery of "peroxisome-like" bodies. It should be noted however, that in these studies staining generally occurred in those ribosomes and reticulum membranes that were adjacent to heavily reactive peroxisomes. This raises the possibility that the observed staining was due to the adsorption of oxidized DAB originating from the peroxisomes. Moreover, even the staining of ribosomes and reticulum membrane that occurs adjacent to *non-reactive* peroxisomes is subject to an interpretation (Novikoff *et al.*, 1972 b) different from that of Wood and Legg (1970).

In view of these considerations it would seem that the staining of ribosomes and endoplasmic reticulum, particularly as it relates to the localization of catalase activity, needs to be scrutinized in a more critical fashion.

Another possible source of artifacts involves the diffusion of hemoproteins. According to Fahimi (1973) the diffuse staining sometimes observed in the vicinity of stained peroxisomes following incubation in DAB media is due to the leakage of catalase from the organelle rather than to diffusion of oxidized DAB. This type of diffusion, which is evident even in well-fixed tissue, apparently occurs during storage of the tissue in buffer, a procedure commonly employed in enzyme cytochemistry. The extent to which hemoprotein diffusion occurs probably depends on factors such as molecular weight and the degree of binding of the enzyme to membranes or other structures (Seligman *et al.*, 1973). It is not yet clear whether such diffusion is limited to catalase or occurs with other hemoproteins. Moreover, the relative importance of diffusion of hemoproteins and diffusion of oxidized DAB in a given situation is uncertain. For instance, Seligman *et al.* (1973) suggest that certain of the staining reactions attributed to diffusion and adsorption of oxidized DAB (Novikoff *et al.*, 1972 b) may be due to diffusion of the hemoprotein.

It is evident from this discussion that the DAB procedures, despite their high resolution, are nevertheless subject to artifacts under certain conditions. Recognition of the type and source of artifacts are especially important when interpreting localizations of DAB oxidative activity in relatively small structures or in restricted sites where diffusion of enzyme or of reaction product over relatively small distances may complicate interpretation of the results. These problems apply not only to the localization of endogenous and exogenous hemoproteins but also to methods such as the immunoenzyme techniques for localizing antigen in which the final step is the visualization of peroxidase activity with the DAB reaction. With such methods, which attempt to detect relatively low levels of activity or minute differences in patterns of deposition of reaction product, recognition of diffusion and adsorption artifacts is especially important.

PEROXIDASES

Peroxidases (donor: hydrogen-peroxide-oxidoreductase, EC 1.11.1.7) catalyze the reduction of hydrogen peroxide to water by electron donors other than peroxide. In the Graham-Karnovsky medium, DAB serves as the electron donor. As already mentioned, the oxidized end product can be visualized by light and electron microscopy. The medium was introduced originally to visualize sites of injected horseradish peroxidase in kidney (see below, "Exogenous Hemoproteins as Tracers"), but has since been applied extensively to the localization of endogenous peroxidases in various types of cells. In addition to polymorphonuclear and eosinophilic leukocytes, which have long been known to possess peroxidase activity (Ackerman, 1968; Bainton and Farquhar, 1968; Miller and Herzog, 1969), the enzyme has been identified in Kupffer cells of liver (Fahimi, 1970; Novikoff *et al.,* 1971a), colon (Venkatachalam *et al.,* 1970), uterus (Brökelmann and Fawcett, 1969), thyroid gland (Strum and Karnovsky, 1970a; Nakai and Fujita, 1970; Novikoff *et al.,* 1971a), salivary gland (Strum and Karnovsky, 1970b; Herzog and Miller, 1970; Novikoff *et al.,* 1971a), and lacrimal gland (Essner, 1971; Herzog and Miller, 1972). A discussion of these localizations is beyond the scope of this chapter, which deals mainly with the cytochemical procedures currently used to localize peroxidase activities at the ultrastructural level. However, it is of interest to note that in the above cases, peroxidase reaction product is demonstrable in the nuclear envelope, endoplasmic reticulum (Fig. 1–2), some Golgi saccules, and secretory granules; these localizations undoubtedly reflect synthesis and packaging of the enzyme in these organelles. Peroxidase activity can also be demonstrated together with acid phosphatase activity in the same section (Beard and Novikoff, 1969; Goldfischer *et al.,* 1970).

One additional point relates to the localization of hemoproteins in the endoplasmic reticulum of hepatic parenchymal cells. As mentioned earlier, peroxidase activity has been demonstrated in the endoplasmic reticulum of Kupffer cells. However, catalase, which is a major constituent of hepatocyte peroxisomes (see below, "Catalase"), has not been visualized so far in the endoplasmic reticulum of these cells. This may reflect the presence of enzymatically inactive precursors. Recent studies indicate that the enzyme in the endoplasmic reticulum is in the form of intermediates, one of which lacks heme, and that its conversion to "authentic," purifiable catalase occurs after transfer to the peroxisomes (Lazarow and de Duve, 1971).

Biochemical studies of the liver microsomal fraction during the past few years have led to the characterization of other important hemoproteins in the endoplasmic reticulum of parenchymal cells; these constitute an electron transport system, quite distinct from that of the mitochondria, which functions in drug and steroid metabolism. The system includes two hemoproteins that theoretically could oxidize DAB; these are: cytochrome b_5, and cytochrome P 450 or carbon-monoxide-binding pigment. Cytochrome b_5 constitutes a significant part of the total microsomal protein, and serves as the natural acceptor for electrons from reduced pyridine nucleotides. Cytochrome P 450 is a proto-heme-containing cytochrome which appears to act as the oxygen-activating enzyme for the microsomal or "mixed function" oxidases. Neither of these cytochromes has as yet been visualized in the endoplasmic reticulum of hepatic parenchymal cells with the DAB procedure. This may be due to insufficient amounts of the proteins or to inherently weak peroxidatic activity. Their identification might be facilitated, however, by studying liver of animals injected with phenobarbital or similar agents. This drug is known to induce synthesis of cytochrome P 450 as part of an adaptive response which results in the enhancement of the capacity for detoxification (Remmer and Merker, 1965).

In contrast to DAB, the related substrates BAXD and BED, referred to previously, are oxidized by both rough and smooth endoplasmic reticulum of liver parenchymal cells, muscle cells, and several plant cells (Seligman et al., 1970; Nir and Seligman, 1971). Unfortunately, the localizations reported so far with these substrates lack the high resolutions obtainable with DAB. The reactions observed with BAXD and BED have been attributed to an unidentified "terminal oxidase" which has not yet been positively identified.

Recent attempts to establish the nature of BED-oxidase have so far succeeded only in proving that it is not monoamine oxidase, xanthine oxidase, peroxidase, cytochrome oxidase, cytochrome P 450, or cytochrome b_5 (Holtzman and Seligman, 1973).

It is of interest to note that certain peroxidases are also demonstrable by virtue of their ability to catalyze the oxidation of polyphenols. Biochemical studies have indicated, for example, that purified lactoperoxidase and horseradish peroxidase will oxidize dihydroxyphenylalanine (DOPA), dopamine, and noradrenalin in a manner analogous to that of tyrosinase (*o*-diphenol: oxygen oxidoreductase, 1.10.3.1) (Bayse and Morrison, 1971). However, the iron porphyrin peroxidases, unlike tyrosinase, require hydrogen peroxide. The oxidation of DOPA by these enzymes provides the basis for a method of localizing endogenous and exogenous (injected) peroxidase activities (van der Ploeg and van Duijn, 1964). The latter has been localized in liver with the electron microscope by taking advantage of the fact that oxidized DOPA is electron-opaque (Daems *et al.,* 1964). Although the DOPA reaction yields an end product similar to that of oxidized DAB, its demonstration requires longer incubation and appears to offer no additional advantages for the demonstration of peroxidase activity.

Sensitivity to Inhibitors

The tissue peroxidases demonstrable by cytochemical means are generally heat-labile, require hydrogen peroxide, and are sensitive to fixatives of high osmolality (Karnovsky, 1965), properties that are not shared by catalase or the nonenzyme hemoproteins (see below). The peroxidases can also be distinguished to some extent on the basis of their responses to inhibitors such as potassium cyanide, sodium azide, excess hydrogen peroxide, and 3-amino, 1,2,4-triazole (AT). Although AT is considered to be a specific inhibitor of catalase, it has also been shown to inhibit peroxidases (see below).

However, the results of inhibitor studies are difficult to interpret, partly because the action of these agents varies considerably from one type of tissue to another. For example, potassium cyanide inhibits peroxidase activity in the uterus (Brökelmann and Fawcett, 1969), submaxillary and lacrimal glands (Strum and Karnovsky, 1970b; Essner, 1971), developing eosinophils (Bainton and Farquhar, 1970), and peritoneal macrophages (Cotran and Litt, 1970), whereas in Kupffer cells of liver (Fahimi, 1970) and mucus-secreting cells of colon (Venkatachalam *et al.,* 1970) the enzyme is insensitive to this agent even at relatively high concentrations. Inhibition of peroxidase activity by sodium azide and excess hydrogen peroxide has also been reported in Kupffer cells of liver (Fahimi, 1970) and in mucus-secreting cells of colon (Venkatachalam *et al.,* 1970). Similarly, peroxidases are completely inhibited by AT in thyroid (Strum and Karnovsky, 1970a) and lacrimal gland (Herzog and Miller, 1972) and partially inhibited in colon (Venkatachalam *et al.,* 1970) and in Kupffer cells of liver (Fahimi, 1970).

In addition to the variations among different cells and tissues mentioned above, peroxidase activities in different sites within the same cell may also vary in their response to inhibitors. For instance, in developing eosinophils,

Table 1-1   Composition of Some Peroxidase Media as Applied to Various Tissues

Tissue	DAB (mg/ml)	% H_2O_2	Reference
Thyroid and submaxillary glands	0.5	0.0003–0.0025	Strum and Karnovsky (1970a and b)
Kidney (exogenous horseradish peroxidase)	0.5	0.001	Graham and Karnovsky (1966b)
Liver (Kupffer cell) and intestine	1.0	0.02	Fahimi (1970); Venkatachalam et al. (1970)
Thyroid, submaxillary, and parotid glands*	2.0	0.01	Novikoff (1970); Novikoff et al. (1971a)
Uterus	0.5	0.002	Brökelmann and Fawcett (1969)

* Contains 0.005M manganese chloride at pH 8.0 or below

peroxidase activity in the endoplasmic reticulum and Golgi saccules is inhibited by potassium cyanide, sodium azide, and AT, whereas in the mature granules it is unaffected by these agents (Bainton and Farquhar, 1970). For additional observations on effects of potassium cyanide and AT on endogenous peroxidases of thyroid, parotid, submaxillary glands, and Kupffer cells of liver, see Novikoff et al. (1971a).

Several modifications of the original DAB medium have been proposed; these are designed to reveal optimal activity of the different peroxidases. The pH of these media is generally between 7.6 and 8.5. As shown in Table 1-1, the concentration of DAB may range from 0.5–2.0 mg/ml, and that of hydrogen peroxide, from 0.0003 to 0.02%; higher concentrations of the latter may be inhibitory. Other forms of peroxide such as sodium or barium peroxide and monoethyl hydrogen peroxide (C_2H_5OOH) could probably also be used (Mitsui, 1960). Barium oxide (BaO_2) placed in a dialysis bag to ensure slow liberation of peroxide has also been used in instances where hydrogen peroxide in the medium was observed to cause tissue damage (Venkatachalam and Fahimi, 1969). Table 1-1 represents a selected list of some media that have been used for demonstrating peroxidase activities in various tissues. The choice of an appropriate medium depends on the particular tissue and on the properties of the peroxidase activity being studied.

CATALASE

Catalase (hydrogen peroxide:hydrogen peroxide oxidoreductase, EC 1.11.1.6) catalyzes the reduction of hydrogen peroxide to water by either of two mechanisms: the peroxidatic reaction, requiring an electron donor; or the catalatic reaction, in which hydrogen peroxide serves as both hydrogen donor and acceptor. In liver and kidney, which contain much higher catalase activities than other mammalian tissues, the enzyme is found mainly in association with peroxisomes. These organelles also contain several hydrogen peroxide-producing oxidases and are thought to be involved in aspects of gluconeogenesis, purine catabolism, and nonphosphorylating respiration. The peroxisome concept has been reviewed in detail (de Duve and Baudhuin, 1966; de Duve, 1969).

Theoretically, the catalase activity in peroxisomes and related particles should be demonstrable cytochemically by means of the peroxidatic reaction referred to above if a suitable chromogenic substrate is provided. Novikoff and Goldfischer (1969) have recently demonstrated peroxisome staining in liver (Fig. 1–3) and kidney, presumably as a result of the peroxidatic activity of catalase, by incubating at an alkaline pH (pH 8 to 9) (37°C) in a medium containing higher concentrations of DAB and hydrogen peroxide (Fig. 1–3). This medium has since been employed by many investigators to study hepatic and renal peroxisomes (Hruban and Rechcigl, 1969).

In general, the staining reaction for peroxisome catalase is dependent on hydrogen peroxide, as was clearly demonstrated by Fahimi (1969),

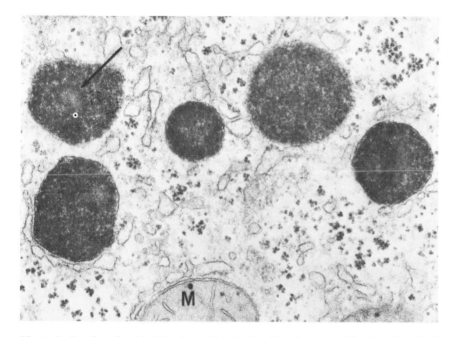

Fig. 1–3. Rat liver fixed in 3% glutaraldehyde for 4 hr. Incubated 60 min in Novikoff and Goldfischer's alkaline DAB medium, pH 9.0. Portion of parenchymal cell showing reaction product localized in five peroxisomes. Inner nucleoid is evident in one (arrow). Product is absent from mitochondrion (*M*) and other elements of cytoplasm. X30,000.

and the activity is resistant to prolonged aldehyde fixation. In lung, this activity apparently survives exposure to a combination of osmium tetroxide and glutaraldehyde (Petrik, 1971).

In addition to peroxisomes, DAB-positive particles sometimes referred to as "peroxisome-like" particles, have been identified in lung (Petrik, 1971; Schneeberger, 1972 a and b), brown adipose tissue (Ahlabo and Barnard, 1971), testis (Reddy and Svoboda, 1972), adrenal cortex (Beard, 1972) and many other tissues (Hruban *et al.*, 1972). In a recent series of studies, Novikoff and colleagues, using a modified DAB medium at pH 9.7 containing potassium cyanide and a high concentration of hydrogen peroxide (Novikoff *et al.*, 1972 a) identified DAB positive particles, which they have termed microperoxisomes, in 24 different mammalian cell types (Novikoff *et al.*, 1973). According to the authors, microperoxisomes can be distinguished from peroxisomes by their shape, intimate association with smooth endoplasmic reticulum and absence of a nucleoid. Many of the peroxisome-like particles described in the literature may correspond to microperoxisomes. The functions of these particles are poorly understood at present. Peroxisome-like particles have also been identified in yeast cells grown under certain conditions (Todd and Vigil, 1972) and in the fat body of insects (Locke and McMahon, 1971).

Catalase-containing organelles have also been identified in plant tissues with the alkaline-DAB method. These include the glyoxysomes of seed endosperms, which possess enzymes involved in conversion of acyl coenzyme A to acetyl coenzyme A, and subsequently to succinate via the glyoxylate cycle (Breidenbach and Beevers, 1967; Beevers, 1969; Vigil, 1970) and the peroxisomes of green leaves which are involved in the metabolism of glycolate (Tolbert and Yamazaki, 1969; Frederick and Newcomb, 1969). Both types of organelles are demonstrable with the same medium used for animal cells, and are therefore not considered further in this chapter.

Evidence that the staining of peroxisomes is due to catalase is provided by studies on the effects of 3-amino-1,2,4-triazole (AT). As mentioned previously, this compound is a potent inhibitor of catalase (Heim *et al.*, 1956) and is believed to act by binding through an amide linkage to the carboxyl groups in the active center of the enzyme (Margoliash and Novogradsky, 1958). The addition of AT to the alkaline DAB medium partially or completely blocks the staining in peroxisomes of virtually all tissues studied (Hirai, 1968; Novikoff and Goldfischer, 1969; Fahimi, 1968); however, see Essner (1970). This effect has also been reported in plant cells (Frederick and Newcomb, 1969). One notable exception is the altered catalase in liver and kidney peroxisomes in a strain of genetically acatalasemic mice, which is largely insensitive to this agent (see below).

The effects of potassium cyanide on catalase activity are more variable, but complete inhibition of activity has been reported in peroxisome-like particles of lung and testis (Petrik, 1971; Reddy and Svoboda, 1972) and in glyoxysomes of castor bean endosperm (Vigil, 1970).

The role of alkalinity in the staining of hepatic and renal peroxisomes was investigated by Goldfischer and Essner (1969) using benzidine as a substrate. They found that peroxisomes do not stain when tissues are incubated in benzidine medium at neutral pH, but are clearly reactive if the tissues are first subjected to alkaline treatment (pH 10 to 12) either during or after fixation in glutaraldehyde. Hirai (1969) obtained similar results by exposing sections of formaldehyde-fixed liver to various denaturants and proteinases. These observations were interpreted as indicating that the various treatments resulted in the dissociation of catalase into peroxidase subunits, which were then capable of oxidizing both benzidine and DAB at neutral pH.

This interpretation is supported by biochemical studies indicating that: (1) denaturation of catalase by acid, alkaline, or peptic digestion results in partial dissociation of the molecule into subunits 50% and 25% as heavy as the native molecule (Tanford and Lovrien, 1962); and (2) that such preparations show progressive loss of catalatic activity and a concomitant enhancement of peroxidatic activity (Inada *et al.,* 1961; for additional references, see Hirai, 1969). It is interesting to note that peroxisomes in a mutant strain of acatalasemic mice (Feinstein, 1970) can be visualized by incubating in DAB media at neutral pH without alkaline or other pretreatment. This is apparently due to the fact that the catalase in these particles is partially dissociated into subunits that have enhanced peroxidase activity (Goldfischer and Essner, 1970). These results have been confirmed by biochemical studies of catalase in this mutant (Feinstein *et al.,* 1971).

Novikoff and Goldfischer's catalase medium
(Novikoff and Goldfischer, 1969)

3,3'-diaminobenzidine tetrahydrochloric acid (Sigma)	20 mg
0.05 M—2-amino-2-methyl-1,3-propandiol buffer, pH 10.0 (Sigma)	9.8 ml
1% hydrogen peroxide (freshly prepared from 30% stock Superoxol, Merck) (final concentration 0.02%)	0.2 ml
Adjust to pH 9.0 and filter if necessary	

For control, incubate in complete medium containing AT (0.01 to 0.001 M) (Novikoff and Goldfischer, 1969). It may be necessary, in some cases, to presoak tissues for 30 to 60 min in the cold in a buffered AT solution before incubation.

NONENZYME HEMOPROTEINS

In addition to peroxidase and catalase, several nonenzyme hemoproteins containing an iron porphyrin prosthetic group exhibit peroxidatic activity, and thus may be demonstrated with DAB procedures. These include: the respiratory proteins, hemoglobin (Fig. 1–4), myoglobin, and cytochrome c; the globin-free compounds, heme, hemin (ferriprotoporphyrin), and hematin (ferriprotoporphyrin hydroxide); and the heme-containing compounds in lysosomes, lipofuscin granules, and neuromelanin particles. According to Pearse (1961), the classical peroxidase reactions are negative in hemosiderin granules, which are considered to contain ferric iron in the

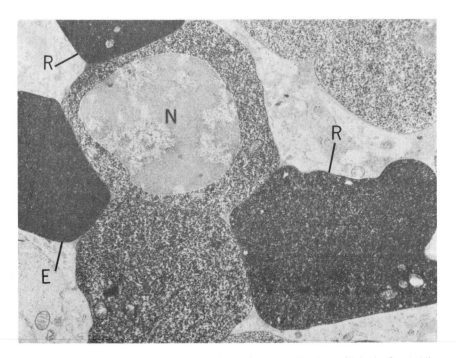

Fig. 1–4. Fetal rat liver, 13 days gestation. Fixed in 3% glutaraldehyde for 1.5 hr and incubated for 30 min in Novikoff and Goldfischer's alkaline DAB medium, pH 9, 37°C. Reaction product in cytoplasm of developing erythroid cells is due to peroxidatic activity of hemoglobin. The nucleated cell (N) is probably an orthochromatic normoblast. Also shown are two reticulocytes (R) and an erythrocyte (E). The difference in amounts of reaction product among these cells is a rough indication of differences in hemoglobin content (Behnke, 1969). X8,000.

form of the hydroxide $Fe(OH)_3$. The reaction is probably also negative for other iron-binding proteins such as lactoferrin and transferrin.

The peroxidatic activity of proteins like hemoglobin is clearly distinguishable from the true peroxidases, discussed above, by their marked resistance to heat and prolonged aldehyde fixation. The intensity of staining of hemoglobin (Behnke, 1969) and myoglobin can also be enhanced by using higher concentrations of DAB and hydrogen peroxide (Goldfischer, 1967; Goldfischer et al., 1970). The localization of cytochrome c and of a heme peptide ("microperoxidase") derived from this protein are discussed in the sections dealing with mitochondrial oxidations and exogenous hemoproteins, respectively.

The staining of lysosomes is probably due to their content of metals. In general, not all lysosomes in a given tissue are demonstrable, and the proportion of reactive granules varies from one tissue to another. For optimal staining, Novikoff (1970) recommends an alkaline medium (pH 8) containing a higher concentration of hydrogen peroxide.

A nonenzymatic heat- and formaldehyde-resistant peroxidatic activity has been described by Goldfischer et al. (1966) in human lipofuscin pigment granules. The reaction is sensitive to cyanide, requires hydrogen peroxide, and persists after extraction of stainable iron with sodium dithionite; it thus resembles the peroxidatic activity characteristic of hemoglobin and related proteins. Accordingly to the authors, the reaction is due to the presence of heme compounds which accumulate within autophagic vacuoles as a result of degradation of cytoplasmic constituents and remain there after the organelles are transformed into lipofuscin granules.

A metal-catalyzed pseudoperoxidase activity that resembles the reaction described above has been demonstrated in the neuromelanin granules of the substantia nigra in monkey and human brain (Barden, 1969). The reaction in these granules is apparently due to their content of copper, which can peroxidatically oxidize DAB. A nonenzymatic, heat-resistant oxidation of DAB has also been reported in norepinephrine-containing cells of the adrenal medulla and in melanosomes and many premelanosomes of two transplantable mouse melanomas (Novikoff et al., 1971b).

DAB OXIDATION IN MITOCHONDRIA

Novikoff and Goldfischer (1969) have shown that mitochondria can also oxidize DAB (Fig. 1–5). For many tissues, optimal staining occurs at a pH of 6.0 with 1/20 the concentration of hydrogen peroxide used to demonstrate peroxisomes. In general, the reaction is insensitive to peroxide and AT, but is inhibited by potassium cyanide and in some instances by sodium azide. Mitochondrial staining, at least in kidney, is also markedly enhanced by the addition of cytochrome c to the medium (Beard and

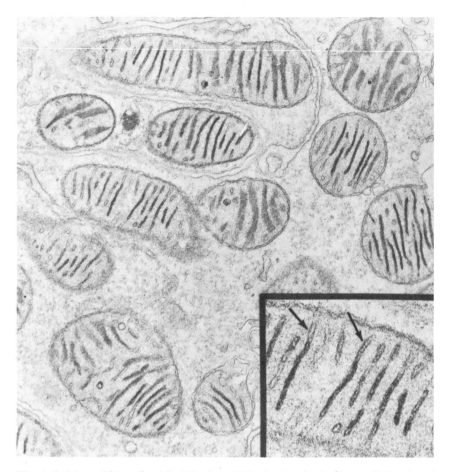

Fig. 1–5. Mouse kidney fixed in 3% glutaraldehyde. Proximal túbule cell. Incubated for 30 min in Novikoff and Goldfischer's alkaline DAB medium, pH 10. Reaction product is localized to space between cristae membranes, but is absent from matrix and from space between outer and inner membranes. It should be noted, however, that this medium is not optimal for mitochondria (see text). The opacity of the cristae membranes (arrows) may be due mainly to lead staining rather than reaction product. X32,000.

Novikoff, 1969). The oxidation of DAB by mitochondria has been observed in many types of plant and animal cells. The intensity of the reaction may vary from one cell type to another, and even among mitochondria in the same cell.

The oxidation of DAB has also been studied in detail in several types of parasite. The reaction is heat-labile and sensitive to potassium cyanide, sodium fluoride, and sodium azide, but insensitive to AT. Most authors have interpreted their findings as indicating the presence of a true mitochondrial peroxidase rather than an oxidase (Threadgold and Read, 1968; Rothman, 1968; Halton, 1969). However, Lumsden *et al.* (1969) consider the reaction as being due to the peroxidatic activity of the cytochromes (see below).

In general, mitochondrial staining is characterized by an accumulation of reaction product in the intracristate space and in the space between the inner and outer membranes. However, the reaction product presumably originates from the activity of hemoproteins residing in the surfaces of these membranes. Since the end product is a relatively large, insoluble complex, it is not likely to traverse the membranes, and apparently accumulates in the spaces between them. It is not entirely clear whether this type of accumulation is due to simple increase in the polymer length of the oxidized DAB (Novikoff *et al.,* 1972 b) or to a spreading of reaction product generated at the surfaces of the membranes (Seligman *et al.,* 1973). When the length of incubation is decreased, the initial deposits of product are demonstrable along the outer surface of the inner membrane and along the inner surface of the outer membrane (Novikoff and Novikoff, 1971; Novikoff *et al.,* 1972 b). Since the inner membrane folds to form the cristae, its outer surface faces both the outer membrane and the intracristate space; its inner surface faces the mitochondrial matrix.

Seligman and colleagues have observed mitochondrial staining in fresh and formaldehyde-fixed tissues using a DAB medium that contains catalase to remove endogenous peroxide and cytochrome c to enhance staining in cells having low levels of this protein (Seligman *et al.,* 1968; Anderson, 1970). These authors demonstrated reaction product in the intracristate space and, in some instances, in the space between inner and outer membranes. They attributed the product in the intracristate space to the activity of enzymes, notably cytochrome oxidase, located on the outer surface of the inner membrane. In addition, they suggested that the reaction could be used as a method for the demonstration of cytochrome oxidase activity, recognizing, however, that the reaction product does not result from the activity of this enzyme per se, but is due to the reduction and oxidation of cytochrome c. This conclusion is also based on the fact that the staining reaction is blocked by potassium cyanide and, to some extent, sodium azide, both of which form a complex with the oxidized form of cytochrome oxidase.

In contrast to the studies by Seligman and colleagues mentioned above, Novikoff and co-workers, using a low pH DAB medium, believe that the reactions in the inner and outer membranes are due to cytochrome c and to a b_5-like cytochrome, respectively (Novikoff and Goldfischer, 1969; Beard and Novikoff, 1969; Novikoff and Novikoff, 1971). They do not consider that the reaction in the inner membrane is due to cytochrome oxidase activity, at least in glutaraldehyde-fixed tissues, since the enzyme is markedly inhibited by this fixative (Sabatini *et al.,* 1963; Novikoff, 1972). Regardless of which cytochrome is being demonstrated in the inner mitochondrial membrane it appears that the actual site of interaction of DAB with the respiratory chain is at cytochrome c (Cammer and Moore, 1973). A possible relationship between the cytochrome c-reducing ability of DAB, benzidine and related compounds and their carcinogenicity has been suggested by Hirai and Yasuhira (1972).

According to Seligman *et al.* (1968) and Barnard *et al.* (1971), the oxidation of DAB observed in the outer mitochondrial membrane could be due either to cytochrome b, as already mentioned, or to monoamine oxidase. However, speculation regarding the latter enzyme hardly seems justified at present, since the question as to its localization in the inner versus the outer membrane is still unresolved (Green *et al.,* 1968; Schnaitman and Greenawalt, 1968).

As already mentioned, BAXD, which is chemically related to DAB, is oxidized by mitochondria as well as other organelles of plant and animal tissues (Nir and Seligman, 1971). The reaction is believed to be due to cytochrome oxidase activity. However, this interpretation is complicated by two factors: (1) preservation of fine structure is generally inadequate, owing to the use of formaldehyde; and (2) BAXD reaction product, at least in some instances, is not homogeneous, but consists of discrete particles that are distributed in irregular patterns on the mitochondrial membranes (Seligman *et al.,* 1970).

The oxidation of DAB has also been described in mitochondria of yeast cells. The reaction is blocked by cyanide, azide, and high levels of hydrogen peroxide. It has been attributed to cytochrome c-peroxidase activity, which is highly active in yeast mitochondria (Hoffman *et al.,* 1970; Todd and Vigil, 1972).

In plant cells, DAB is oxidized by chloroplasts as well as by mitochondria. The chloroplast reaction is photosensitive, occurring only when the organelles are illuminated; in the absence of light, only the mitochondria are reactive. In chloroplasts of spinach and *Elodea* leaves, reaction product is associated with the thylakoid membranes where they are differentiated into grana stacks and stroma, but is absent from the outer, limiting membranes (Nir and Seligman, 1970). The enzymes responsible for the photooxidation of DAB in chloroplasts have not yet been identified.

Novikoff and Goldfischer's acid DAB medium
(Novikoff and Goldfischer, 1969)

3,3′-diaminobenzidine tetra HCl (Sigma)	20 mg
0.05 M sodium acetate-acetic acid buffer (pH 5.0)	8.9 ml
0.1 hydrogen peroxide (freshly prepared from 30% stock, Superoxol, Merck) (final concentration 0.001%)	8.9 ml

0.05 M manganese chloride   1.0 ml
Adjust to pH 6.0 and filter if necessary

EXOGENOUS HEMOPROTEINS AS TRACERS

The use of exogenous (injected) horseradish peroxidase (HRP) as a tracer was first suggested by Straus (1957), who showed that the injected protein could be visualized by light microscopy after incubation in benzidine media. The subject has been reviewed in detail by Straus (1969). As mentioned previously, benzidine has not been used extensively at the ultrastructural level. It should be noted also that peroxidase and hemoglobin possess considerable inherent opacity, and were used previously as tracers without incubation in studies of kidney (Miller, 1960; Novikoff, 1963; Ericsson, 1964). With the introduction of the DAB procedure, it became possible to compare the uptake and transport of hemoproteins of different sizes by visualizing their peroxidatic activities (Fig. 1–6). Of

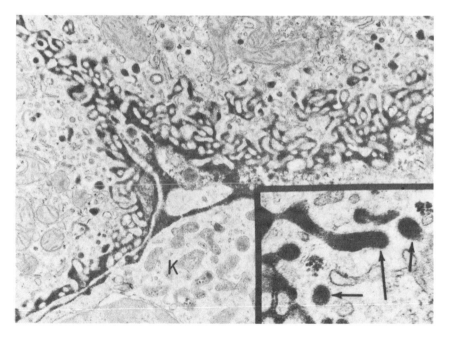

Fig. 1–6. Mouse liver, 2 min after intravenous injection of 10 mg horseradish peroxidase. Fixed in glutaraldehyde-acrolein, incubated 10 min in DAB medium, pH 7.4, 37°C (Fahimi, 1970). Reaction product fills sinusoid and is present in numerous invaginations at surface of parenchymal cells. Part of Kupffer (K) cells is shown. X48,000. Inset shows coated vesicles containing reaction product (short arrows); some are in process of formation from the infoldings (long arrow). X15,000.

particular interest are those tracers that are comparable in molecular weight to naturally occurring proteins. For example, the molecular weight of lactoperoxidase is only slightly greater than plasma albumin.

The hemoprotein tracers commonly employed at present are listed in Table 1–2, and are arranged according to their molecular weights. It should

Table 1–2   Molecular Weight and Source of Some Common Hemoprotein Tracers

Hemoprotein and Source	Approximate M.W.	Reference
"Microperoxidase" (horse heart cytochrome c)	1,900	Feder (1970; 1971)
Cytochrome c (horse heart)	12,000	Karnovsky and Rice (1969)
Myoglobin (horse or whale skeletal muscle)	17,500	Anderson (1972)
Peroxidase (horseradish)	40,000	Graham and Karnovsky (1966a)
Hemoglobin (rat, human and bovine erythrocytes)	68,000	Goldfischer et al. (1970)
Lactoperoxidase (bovine milk)	82,000	Graham and Kellermeyer (1968)
Myeloperoxidase (human leukocytes)	160,000–180,000	Graham and Karnovsky (1966b)
Catalase (bovine liver)	240,000	Venkatachalam and Fahimi (1969)

be noted that the procedures for demonstrating these proteins are essentially the same as those employed to visualize endogenous activities (Fig. 1–6). However, the proteins taken up by most tissues are usually present in much higher concentrations, and are therefore often demonstrable by using shorter periods of incubation. The controls are also the same, but include, in addition, means of minimizing artifacts arising from enzyme diffusion (see below). As in the case of the endogenous enzymes, the activities of injected hemoproteins can be visualized together with certain phosphatase activities in the same tissue section (Creemers and Jacques, 1971).

Factors Affecting Localization of Exogenous Peroxidase

Cotran and colleagues (Cotran and Karnovsky, 1967, 1968; Cotran et al., 1968) have shown that local or parenteral injection of HRP into noninbred rats or guinea pigs induces degranulation of mast cells, which, in turn, results in increased permeability of small blood vessels, particularly venules, and an "anaphylactoid" reaction. This response can be suppressed by prior administration of histamine and serotonin antagonists. Whether the reaction is due to an impurity is not known, but all commercial preparations tested (Sigma, types I to VI) were effective inducers of vascular leakage. According to the authors, HRP, which has a high content of carbohydrate, behaves like dextran in its action on mast cells. Wistar-Furth strain rats as well as mice (Karnovsky, 1967) appear to be resistant to the mast cell damaging effects of peroxidase, at least in the dosages generally employed.

Another source of artifact relates to the propensity of exogenous HRP and possibly other hemoproteins to diffuse after being taken up by tissues. According to Straus (1964), intravenously injected HRP, particularly at high concentrations, may be released during fixation from initial sites of deposition and be subsequently adsorbed to other structures, especially nuclei and plasma membranes. In order to minimize this effect, he stresses the use of small tissue blocks that have been thoroughly fixed with large volumes of fixative containing sucrose. Several types of control experiments have been suggested to minimize this type of artifact (Graham and Karnovsky, 1966a; Cotran and Karnovsky, 1968).

A final point worth mentioning relates to the purity of the commercial preparations used as exogenous tracers. It is not entirely clear whether this is a significant factor in the uptake and transport of exogenous proteins. For instance, horseradish peroxidase type II (Sigma), which is used by most investigators, contains a substantial amount of carbohydrate, and is separable by starch gel electrophoresis into multiple, enzymatically active components; however, these do not differ appreciably in absorption spectrum, enzyme activity, or amino acid composition (Klapper and Hackett, 1965). Moreover, Karnovsky (1967), in a study of capillary permeability, observed no differences between the above preparation and two highly purified preparations—peroxidase type VI (Sigma), and an electrophoretically purified peroxidase (Worthington Corp.). Although no significant differences in protein transport have been attributed so far to the purity of peroxidase or other hemoproteins, the use of purified preparations having higher enzymatic activity may be advantageous in detecting small amounts of injected proteins (Clementi, 1970).

Cytochrome c

Karnovsky and Rice (1969) showed that cytochrome c could be visualized after injection into animals by incubating the tissues in a DAB medium at acid pH containing chloride ions and a relatively high concentration of hydrogen peroxide. The rationale for the method derives from biochemical studies by Flatmark (1965), who showed that the inherently low peroxidatic activity of cytochrome c could be activated in the presence of certain ions, low pH, and high peroxide concentrations. Paleus et al. (1955) had earlier shown that a ferriporphyrin c peptide consisting of heme and 11 amino acids could be obtained by peptic digestion of cytochrome c, and that this peptide displayed a 20-fold higher peroxidatic activity at acid pH than did the untreated protein. The activation of cytochrome c peroxidatic activity appears to be akin to the dissociation of catalase into subunits, described above.

Feder (1970, 1971) has also utilized this concept in preparing a heme peptide fragment from cytochrome c ("microperoxidase") by means of peptic digestion. The resulting protein displays enhanced peroxidatic activity that is demonstrable with the DAB procedure; it has a molecular weight of about 1,900, and represents the smallest of the hemoprotein tracers so far available (Table 1–2).

The cytochrome c medium indicated below was modified in our laboratory.

Cytochrome c medium, modified after Karnovsky and Rice (1969)

Preincubation (to enhance penetration of DAB):
  3,3'-diaminobenzidine tetra HCl (Sigma)
  0.05 M Tris HCl or 0.2 M cacodylate buffer (pH 7.4–7.6)   10 ml
Soak sections for 3 hr at 4°C.
Incubation:
  3.3'-diaminobenzidine tetra HCl (Sigma)   5 mg
  0.1 M Na citrate buffer (pH 3.9)   10 ml
  1% hydrogen peroxide (freshly prepared from 30% stock
  Superoxol, Merck) (final concentration 0.05%)   0.5 ml

Distinguishing Endogenous from Exogenous Activities

It is evident from the preceding discussion that the DAB procedures are applicable to hemoproteins of both endogenous and exogenous origin provided sufficient residual activity remains in the tissue after fixation. However, injected hemoproteins may sometimes be difficult to identify in those tissues that also possess substantial endogenous activity. The two activities can, however, frequently be distinguished by their differing sensitivities to aldehyde fixation. This has clearly been demonstrated in peritoneal macrophages, which possess an endogenous peroxidase in the endoplasmic reticulum (Fahimi, 1970). When these cells are exposed *in vitro* to horseradish peroxidase, the ingested protein is demonstrable within phagocytic vacuoles. However, the activity in the endoplasmic reticulum is completely inhibited by exposure to glutaraldehyde-formaldehyde (3 to 5 hr at room temperature), whereas that of the ingested protein, as noted earlier by Graham and Karnovsky (1966a), is not substantially affected. Cytochrome c and "microperoxidase" are apparently also resistant to glutaraldehyde-formaldehyde fixation; the latter activity survives a 24 hr (4°C) exposure to this fixative (Feder, 1971). However, the peroxidase activity of hemoproteins may vary in reactivity. For instance, the peroxidatic activity of catalase is much more resistant to aldehyde fixation than are the true peroxidases, and thus more difficult to inhibit by prolonged fixation.

As mentioned previously, high concentrations of hydrogen peroxide also inhibit peroxidase activities in the endoplasmic reticulum of certain cells. In such instances, this may serve as an additional means of eliminating endogenous activity.

It is evident from this discussion that the study of exogenous hemoproteins must be accompanied by suitable controls in which the levels of endogenous activities that survive fixation can be independently assessed.

CONCLUDING REMARKS

The methodology for localizing hemoproteins at the ultrastructural level has been briefly surveyed in this chapter. As already mentioned, no attempt has been made to review the entire literature that has accumulated as a result of the application of the DAB procedures. The biological findings have been considered only insofar as they illustrate the applications and limitations of the procedures.

By almost any criterion, the DAB reaction emerges as one of the most sensitive and versatile cytochemical staining methods available. In addition to demonstrating endogenous and exogenous activities, certain hemoproteins have also been used in immunochemical reactions, as antigens for detecting sites of antibody synthesis in immunocompetent cells, and as antibody markers for the detection of antigenic sites. In both instances, the antigen-antibody complex is visualized by taking advantage of the peroxidase activity of the hemoprotein component. These aspects of hemoprotein cytochemistry have not been included in this chapter, since they are dealt with in detail by Sternberger (1973) in Volume I.

It is clear that the DAB procedures are capable of detecting many of the enzymes representing the main classes of hemoproteins in plant and animal cells. What remains undetermined is to what extent potentially demonstrable proteins escape detection by these methods. One such example, cytochrome P 450, in the endoplasmic reticulum of hepatic parenchymal cells, has already been mentioned. It is possible that other proteins also remain undetected either because they are not present in sufficient amounts or because their activity is masked or too weak to be visualized with presently available media.

In addition to its use in hemoprotein cytochemistry, DAB may have another important virtue—it may serve as a basis for the design of new substrates with similar properties, including the important characteristic of forming polymeric complexes with osmium tetroxide. Some attempts in this direction have already been referred to in this chapter. The availability of such substrates may open the way to mapping other enzymes with the same degree of precision that has distinguished the study of hemoproteins.

ACKNOWLEDGMENTS

The author is indebted to Dr. Etienne de Harven, Dr. Constance Oliver, and Dr. Sidney Goldfischer for reading the manuscript and providing important suggestions. My thanks also to: Dr. Oliver for supplying the electron micrograph shown in Fig. 1–4; Mr. William Matz for preparing the photographs; and Mrs. Dorothy Saltzer for typing the manuscript.

The work was supported, in part, by United States Public Health Service Grant CA-08748.

REFERENCES

Ackerman, G. A. (1968). Ultrastructure and cytochemistry of the developing neutrophil. *Lab. Invest.* **19**, 290.

Agner, S. (1941). Verdoperoxidase. *Acta Physiol. Scand.* **2** (supp. 8), 5.

Ahlabo, I., and Barnard, T. (1971). Observations on peroxisomes in brown adipose tissue of the rat. *J. Histochem. Cytochem.* **19**, 670.

Anderson, W. A. (1970). The localization of cytochrome c oxidase activity during mitochondrial specialization in spermiogenesis of prosobranch snails. *J. Histochem. Cytochem.* **18**, 201.

Anderson, W. A. (1972). The use of exogenous myoglobin as an ultrastructural tracer: Reabsorption and translocation of protein by the renal tubule. *J. Histochem. Cytochem.* **20**, 672.

Bainton, D. F., and Farquhar, M. G. (1968). Differences in enzyme content of azurophil and specific granules of polymorphonuclear leukocytes. II. Cytochemistry and electron microscopy of bone marrow cells. *J. Cell Biol.* **39**, 299.

Bainton, D. F., and Farquhar, M. G. (1970). Segregation and packaging of granule enzymes in eosinophilic leukocytes. *J. Cell. Biol.* **45**, 54.

Barden, H. (1969). The histochemical relationship of neuromelanin and lipofuscin. *J. Neuropath. Exptl. Neurol.* **28**, 419.

Barnard, T., Afzelius, B. A., and Lindberg, O. (1971). A cytochemical investigation into the distribution of cytochrome oxidase activity within the mitochondria of brown adipose tissue from the prenatal rat. *J. Ultrastruct. Res.* **34**, 544.

Bayse, G. S., and Morrison, M. (1971). The role of peroxidase in catalyzing oxidation of polyphenols. *Biochem. Biophys. Acta* **244**, 77.

Beard, M. E. (1972). Identification of peroxisomes in the rat adrenal cortex. *J. Histochem. Cytochem.* **20**, 173.

Beard, M. E., and Novikoff, A. B. (1969). Distribution of peroxisomes (microbodies) in the nephron of the rat: A cytochemical study. *J. Cell Biol.* **42**, 501.

Beevers, H. (1969). Glyoxysomes of castor bean endosperm and their relation to gluconeogenesis. *Ann. N. Y. Acad. Sci.* **168**, 313.

Behnke, O. (1969). Demonstration of endogenous peroxidase activity in the electron microscope. *J. Histochem. Cytochem.* **17,** 62.

Breidenbach, R. W., and Beevers, H. (1967). Association of the glyoxylate cycle enzymes in a novel subcellular particle from castor bean endosperm. *Biochem. Biophys. Res. Commun.* **27,** 462.

Brökelmann, J., and Fawcett, D. W. (1969). The localization of endogenous peroxidase in the rat uterus and its induction by estradiol. *Biol. Reprod.* **1,** 59.

Burstone, M. S. (1960). Histochemical demonstration of cytochrome oxidase with new amine reagents. *J. Histochem. Cytochem.* **8,** 63.

Cammer, W., and Moore, C. L. (1973). Oxidation of 3,3'-diaminobenzidine by rat liver mitochondria. *Biochem.* **12,** 2502.

Clementi, F. (1970). Effect of horseradish peroxidase on mice lung capillaries' permeability. *J. Histochem. Cytochem.* **18,** 887.

Cotran, R. S., and Karnovsky, M. J. (1967). Vascular leakage induced by horseradish peroxidase in the rat. *Proc. Soc. Exp. Biol. Med.* **126,** 557.

Cotran, R. S., and Karnovsky, M. J. (1968). Ultrastructural studies on the permeability of the mesothelium to horseradish peroxidase. *J. Cell. Biol.* **37,** 123.

Cotran, R. S., Karnovsky, M. J., and Goth, A. (1968). Resistance of Wistar/ Furth rats to the mast cell-damaging effect of horseradish peroxidase. *J. Histochem. Cytochem.* **16,** 382.

Cotran, R. S., and Litt, M. (1970). Ultrastructural localization of horseradish peroxidase and endogenous peroxidase activity in guinea pig peritoneal macrophages. *J. Immunol.* **105,** 1536.

Creemers, J., and Jacques, P. J. (1971). Endocytic uptake and vesicular transport of injected horseradish peroxidase in the vacuolar apparatus of rat liver cells. *Exp. Cell Res.* **67,** 188.

Czaninski, Y., and Catesson, A. M. (1970). Activities peroxydasiques d'origines diverses dans les cellules d'*Acer pseudoplatanus* (tissus conducteurs et cellules en culture). *J. Microscopie* **9,** 1089.

Daems, W. Th., van der Ploeg, M., Persijn, J. P., and van Duijn, P. (1964). Demonstration with the electron microscope of injected peroxidase in rat liver cells. *Histochemie* **3,** 561.

de Duve, C. (1969). Evolution of the peroxisome. *Ann. N. Y. Acad. Sci.* **168,** 396.

de Duve, C., and Baudhuin, P. (1966). Peroxisomes (microbodies and related particles). *Physiol. Rev.* **46,** 323.

Dvorak, A. M., Dvorak, H. F., and Karnovsky, M. J. (1972). Cytochemical localization of peroxidase activity in the developing erythrocyte. *Am. J. Path.* **67,** 303.

Ericsson, J. L. E. (1964). Absorption and decomposition of homologous hemoglobin in renal proximal tubular cells. *Acta Path. Microbiol. Scand.,* Suppl. Ad 168.

Essner, E. (1970). Observations on hepatic and renal peroxisomes (microbodies) in the developing chick. *J. Histochem. Cytochem.* **18,** 80.

Essner, E. (1971). Localization of endogenous peroxidase in rat exorbital lacrimal gland. *J. Histochem. Cytochem.* **19,** 216.

Essner, E. (1973). Phosphatases. In: *Electron Microscopy of Enzymes: Principles and Methods,* Vol. 1 (Hayat, M. A., ed.). Van Nostrand Reinhold Company, New York and London.

Fahimi, H. D. (1968). Cytochemical localization of peroxidase activity in rat hepatic microbodies (peroxisomes). *J. Histochem. Cytochem.* **16,** 547.

Fahimi, H. D. (1969). Cytochemical localization of peroxidatic activity of catalase in rat hepatic microbodies (peroxisomes). *J. Cell Biol.* **43,** 275.

Fahimi, H. D. (1970). The fine structural localization of endogenous and exogenous peroxidase activity in Kupffer cells of rat liver. *J. Cell Biol.* **47,** 247.

Fahimi, H. D. (1971). Morphogenesis of peroxisomes in rat liver. Abstracts of the American Society of Cell Biology, New Orleans, La., 87.

Fahimi, H. D. (1973). Diffusion artifacts in cytochemistry of catalase. *J. Histochem. Cytochem.* **21,** 999.

Feder, N. (1970). A heme-peptide as an ultrastructural tracer. *J. Histochem. Cytochem.* **18,** 911.

Feder, N. (1971). Microperoxidase. An ultrastructural tracer of low molecular weight. *J. Cell Biol.* **51,** 339.

Feinstein, R. N. (1970). Acatalasemia in the mouse and other species. *Biochem. Genetics* **4,** 135.

Feinstein, R. N., Savol, R., and Howard, J. B. (1971). Conversion of catalatic to peroxidatic activity in livers of normal and acatalasemic mice. *Enzymologia* **41,** 345.

Fischel, R. (1910). Der histochemische Nachweis der Peroxydase. *Wien. Klin, Woch.* **23,** 1557.

Flatmark, T. (1965). Studies on the peroxidase effect of cytochrome c. IV. The influence of pH and certain anions on the over-all reaction. *Acta Chemica Scand.* **19,** 2059.

Frederick, S. E., and Newcomb, E. H. (1969). Cytochemical localization of catalase in leaf microbodies (peroxisomes). *J. Cell Biol.* **43,** 343.

Goldfischer, S. (1967). The cytochemical localization of myoglobin in striated muscle of man and walrus. *J. Cell Biol.* **34,** 398.

Goldfischer, S., and Essner, E. (1969). Further observations on the peroxidatic activities of microbodies (peroxisomes). *J. Histochem. Cytochem.* **17,** 681.

Goldfischer, S., and Essner, E. (1970). Peroxidase activity in peroxisomes (microbodies) of acatalasemic mice. *J. Histochem. Cytochem.* **18,** 482.

Goldfischer, S., Novikoff, A. B., Albala, A., and Biempica, L. (1970). Hemoglobin uptake by rat hepatocytes and its breakdown within lysosomes. *J. Cell Biol.* **44,** 513.

Goldfischer, S., and Schiller, E. (1971). The hemoglobin cells of *Gastrophilus intestinalis*; a cytochemical study. *J. Microscopie* **10,** 305.

Goldfischer, S., Villaverde, H., and Forschirm, R. (1966). The demonstration of acid hydrolase, thermostable reduced diphosphopyridine nucleotide tetrazolium reductase and peroxidase activities in human lipofuscin pigment granules. *J. Histochem. Cytochem.* **14,** 641.

Graham, G. S. (1918). Benzidine as a peroxidase reagent for blood smears and tissues. *J. Med. Res.* **39,** 15.

Graham, R. C., and Karnovsky, M. J. (1966a). The early stages of absorption of injected horseradish peroxidase in the proximal tubules of mouse kidney. Ultrastructural cytochemistry by a new technique. *J. Histochem. Cytochem.* **14,** 291.

Graham, R. C., and Karnovsky, M. J. (1966b). Glomerular permeability. Ultrastructural cytochemical studies using peroxidases as protein tracers. *J. Exp. Med.* **124,** 1123.

Graham, R. C., and Kellermeyer, R. W. (1968). Bovine lactoperoxidase as a cytochemical protein tracer for electron microscopy. *J. Histochem. Cytochem.* **16,** 275.

Graham, R. C., Lundholm, U., and Karnovsky, M. J. (1965). Cytochemical demonstration of peroxidase activity with 3-amino-9-ethylcarbazole. *J. Histochem. Cytochem.* **13,** 150.

Green, D. E., Allmann, D. W., Harris, R. A., and Tan, W. C. (1968). Enzyme localization in the inner and outer mitochondrial membranes. *Biochem. Biophys. Res. Comm.* **31,** 368.

Halton, D. W. (1969). Peroxidase activity in the trematode *Haplometra cylindracea. Exp. Parasit.* **24,** 265.

Hanker, J. S., Kasler, F., Bloom, M. G., Copeland, J. S., and Seligman, A. M. (1967). Coordination polymers of osmium: The nature of osmium black. *Science* **156,** 1737.

Hanker, J. S., Anderson, W. A., and Bloom, F. E. (1972a). Osmiophilic polymer generation: Catalysis by transition metal compounds in ultrastructural cytochemistry. *Science* **175,** 991.

Hanker, J. S., Yates, P. E., Clapp, D. H., and Anderson, W. A. (1972b). New methods for the demonstration of lysosomal hydrolases by the formation of osmium blacks. *Histochemie* **30,** 201.

Hayat, M. A. (1970). *Principles and Techniques of Electron Microscopy: Biological Applications,* Vol. 1. Van Nostrand Reinhold Company, New York and London.

Hayat, M. A. (1972). *Basic Electron Microscopy Techniques.* Van Nostrand Reinhold Company, New York and London.

Hayat, M. A., ed. (1973). Specimen preparation. In: *Electron Microscopy of Enzymes: Principles and Methods,* Vol. 1. Van Nostrand Reinhold Company, New York and London.

Heim, W. G., Appleman, D., and Pyfrom, H. T. (1956). Effects of 3-amino-1, 2,4-triazole (AT) on catalase and other compounds. *Amer. J. Physiol.* **186,** 19.

Herzog, V., and Miller, F. (1970). Die Lokalisation endogener Peroxydase in der Glandula parotis der Ratte. *Z. Zellforsch.* **107,** 403.

Herzog, V., and Miller, F. (1972). The localization of endogenous peroxidase in the lacrimal gland of the rat during postnatal development: Electron microscope cytochemical and biochemical studies. *J. Cell Biol.* **53,** 662.

Hirai, K.-I. (1968). Specific affinity of oxidized amine dye (radical intermediate) for heme enzymes: Study in microscopy and spectrophotometry. *Acta Histochem. Cytochem.* (Kyoto) **1,** 43.

Hirai, K.-I. (1969). Light microscopic study of the peroxidatic activity of catalase in formaldehyde-fixed rat liver. *J. Histochem. Cytochem.* **17,** 585.

Hirai, K.-I. (1971). Comparison between 3,3'-diaminobenzidine and auto-oxidized 3,3'-diaminobenzidine in the cytochemical demonstration of oxidative enzymes. *J. Histochem. Cytochem.* **19,** 434.

Hirai, K-I., and Yasuhira, K. (1972). Mitochondrial oxidation of 3,3'-diaminobenzidine and related compounds and their possible relation to carcinogenesis. *Gann* **63,** 665.

Hoffman, H. P., Szabo, A., and Avers, C. (1970). Cytochemical localization of catalase activity in yeast peroxisomes. *J. Bacteriol.* **104,** 581.

Holtzman, J. L., and Seligman, A. M. (1973). The oxidation of N,N'-bis-(4-

aminophenyl)-N,N′-dimethylethylenediamine (BED) by rat liver. *Arch. Biochem. Biophys.* **155**, 237.

Hruban, Z., and Rechcigl, M. (1969). Microbodies and related particles: Morphology, biochemistry, and physiology. *Int. Rev. Cytol.,* Suppl. **1**, 20.

Hruban, Z., Vigil, E., Slesers, A., and Hopkins, E. (1972). Microbodies. Constituent organelles of animal cells. *Lab. Invest.* **27**, 184.

Inada, Y., Kurozumi, T., and Shibata, K. (1961). Peroxidase activity of hemoproteins. I. Generation of activity by acid or alkali denaturation of methemoglobin and catalase. *Arch. Biochem. Biophys.* **93**, 30.

Karnovsky, M. J. (1965). A formaldehyde-glutaraldehyde fixative of high osmolarity for use in electron microscopy. *J. Cell Biol.* **27**, 137A.

Karnovsky, M. J. (1967). The ultrastructural basis of capillary permeability studied with peroxidase as a tracer. *J. Cell Biol.* **35**, 213.

Karnovsky, M. J., and Rice, D. F. (1969). Exogenous cytochrome c as an ultrastructural tracer. *J. Histochem. Cytochem.* **17**, 751.

Klapper, M. H., and Hackett, D. P. (1965). Investigations on the multiple components of commercial horseradish peroxidase. *Biochim. Biophys. Acta* **96**, 272.

Lazarow, P. B., and de Duve, C (1971). Intermediates in the biosynthesis of peroxisomal catalase in rat liver. *Biochem. Biophys. Res. Commun.* **45**, 1198.

Legg, P. G., and Wood, R. L. (1970). New observations on microbodies: A cytochemical study on CPIB-treated rat liver. *J. Cell Biol.* **45**, 118.

Locke, M., and McMahon, J. T. (1971). The origin and fate of microbodies in the fat body of an insect. *J. Cell Biol.* **48**, 61.

Lumsden, R. D., Oaks, J. A., and Mills, R. R. (1969). Mitochondrial oxidation of diaminobenzidine and its relationship to the cytochemical localization of tapeworm peroxidase. *J. Parasit.* **55**, 1119.

Margoliash, E., and Novogrodsky, A. (1958). A study of the inhibition of catalase by 3-amino-1,2,4-triazole. *Biochem. J.* **68**, 468.

Miller, F. (1960). Hemoglobin absorption by the cells of the proximal convoluted tubule in mouse kidney. *J. Biophys. Biochem. Cytol.* **8**, 689.

Miller, F., and Herzog, V. (1969). Die Lokalisation von Peroxydase und sauer Phosphatase in eosinophilen Leukocyten wahrend der Reifung. Elektronenmikroskopisch-cytochemische Untersuchungen am Knockenmark von Ratte und Kaninchen. *Z. Zellforsch.* **97**, 84.

Mitsui, T. (1960). Application of the electron microscope to the cytochemical peroxidase reaction in salamander leukocytes. *J. Biophys. Biochem. Cytol.* **7**, 251.

Nakai, Y., and Fujita, H. (1970). Fine structural localization of peroxidase in the rat thyroid. *Z. Zellforsch.* **107**, 104.

Nir, I., and Seligman, A. M. (1970). Photooxidation of diaminobenzidine (DAB) by chloroplast lamellae. *J. Cell Biol.* **46**, 617.

Nir, I., and Seligman, A. M. (1971). Ultrastructural localization of oxidase activities in corn root tip cells with two new osmiophilic reagents compared to diaminobenzidine. *J. Histochem. Cytochem.* **19**, 611.

Novikoff, A. B. (1963). Lysosomes in the physiology and pathology of cells: Contributions of staining methods. In *Ciba Foundation Symposium on Lysosomes* (de Reuck, A. V. S., and Cameron, M. P., eds.), p. 36. Little, Brown, Boston.

Novikoff, A. B. (1970). Visualization of cell organelles by diaminobenzidine reactions. In *Proceedings of the Seventh International Congress on Electron*

Microscopy (Favard, P., ed.), p. 565. Societe Francaise de Microscopie Electronique, Paris.

Novikoff, A. B. (1972). Personal communication.

Novikoff, A. B., Beard, M. E., Albala, A., Sheid, B., Quintana, N., and Biempica, L. (1971a). Localization of endogenous peroxidases in animal tissues. *J. Microscopie* **12**, 381.

Novikoff, A. B., Biempica, L., Beard, M., and Domonitz, R. (1971b). Visualization by diaminobenzidine of norepinephrine cells. Premelanosomes and melanosomes. *J. Microscopie* **12**, 297.

Novikoff, A. B., and Goldfischer, S. (1969). Visualization of peroxisomes (microbodies) and mitochondria with diaminobenzidine. *J. Histochem. Cytochem.* **17**, 675.

Novikoff, A. B., and Novikoff, P. M. (1971). Cytochemical staining reactions for enzymes in cytoplasmic organelles. *Biomembranes*, **2**, 33.

Novikoff, A. B., Novikoff, P. M., Davis, C., and Quintana, N. (1972a). Studies of microperoxisomes II. A cytochemical method for light and electron microscopy. *J. Histochem. Cytochem.* **20**, 1006.

Novikoff, A. B., Novikoff, P. M., Quintana, N., and Davis, C. (1972b). Diffusion artifacts in 3,3'-diaminobenzidine cytochemistry. *J. Histochem. Cytochem.* **20**, 745.

Novikoff, A. B., Novikoff, P. M., Davis, C., and Quintana, N. (1973). Studies on microperoxisomes. V. Are microperoxisomes ubiquitous in mammalian cells? *J. Histochem. Cytochem.* **21**, 737.

Ornstein, L. (1968). Benzidine analogues used with α-naphthol in new variants of oxidase and peroxidase cytochemical reactions. 19th Ann. Meeting, Histochem. Soc., New Orleans, p. 6.

Paleus, S., Ehrenberg, A., and Tuppy, H. (1955). Study of a peptic degradation product of cytochrome c. II. Investigation of the linkage between peptide moiety and prosthetic group. *Acta Chemica Scand.* **9**, 365.

Paul, K. G. (1963). Peroxidases. In: The Enzymes, 2d ed. (Boyer, P. D., Lardy, H., and Myrback, K. eds.), Vol. 8, p. 227. Academic Press, New York.

Pearse, A. G. E. (1961). Histochemistry. Theoretical and Applied. 2d ed. Little, Brown, Boston.

Petrik, P. (1971). Fine structural identification of peroxisomes in mouse and rat bronchiolar and alveolar epithelium. *J. Histochem. Cytochem.* **19**, 339.

Poux, N. (1969). Localisation d'activités enzymatiques dans les cellules du méristèmes radiculaire de *Cucumis sativus* L. II. activité peroxydasique. *J. Microscopie* **8**, 855.

Reddy, J., and Svoboda, D. (1972). Microbodies (peroxisomes): identification in interstitial cells of the testis. *J. Histochem. Cytochem.* **20**, 140.

Remmer, H., and Merker, H. J. (1965). Effect of drugs on the formation of smooth endoplasmic reticulum and drug-metabolizing enzymes. *Ann. N. Y. Acad. Sci.* **123**, 79.

Rigatsu, J. L., Legg, P. G., and Wood, R. L. (1970). Microbody formation in regenerating rat liver. *J. Histochem. Cytochem.* **18**, 893.

Roels, F. (1970). Localisation d'activités peroxydasiques dans l'oeuf d'*Artemia salina*, a l'aide de 3,3'-diaminobenzidine, de benzidine et de pyrogallol. *Arch. Biol.* (Liege), **81**, 229.

Rothman, A. H. (1968). Peroxidase activity in platyhelminth cuticular mitochondria. *Exp. Parasit.* **23**, 51.

Sabatini, D. D., Bensch, K., and Barrnett, R. J. (1963). Cytochemistry and electron microscopy: The preservation of cellular ultrastructure and enzymatic activity by aldehyde fixation. *J. Cell Biol.* **17,** 19.

Schnaitman, C., and Greenawalt, J. W. (1968). Enzymatic properties of the inner and outer membranes of rat liver mitochondria. *J. Cell Biol.* **38,** 158.

Schneeberger, E. E. (1972a). A comparative study of microbodies (peroxisomes) in great alveolar cells of rodents, rabbits and monkeys. *J. Histochem. Cytochem.* **20,** 180.

Schneeberger, E. E. (1972b). Development of peroxisomes in granular pneumocytes during pre- and postnatal growth. *Lab. Invest.* **27,** 581.

Seligman, A. M., Karnovsky, M. J., Wasserkrug, H. L., and Hanker, J. S. (1968). Non-droplet ultrastructural demonstration of cytochrome oxidase activity with a polymerizing osmiophilic reagent, diaminobenzidine (DAB). *J. Cell Biol.* **38,** 1.

Seligman, A. M., Wasserkrug, H. L., and Plapinger, R. E. (1970). Comparison of the ultrastructural demonstration of cytochrome oxidase activity with three bis (phenylenediamines). *Histochemie* **23,** 63.

Seligman, A. M., Shannon, W. A., Hoshino, Y., and Plapinger, R. E. (1973). Some important principles in 3,3'-diaminobenzidine ultrastructural cytochemistry. *J. Histochem. Cytochem.* **21,** 765.

Sternberger, L. A. (1973). Enzyme immunocytochemistry. In: *Electron Microscopy of Enzymes: Principles and Methods,* Vol. 1 (Hayat, M. A., ed.). Van Nostrand Reinhold Company, New York and London.

Straus, W. (1957). Segregation of an intravenously injected protein by "droplets" of the cells of rat kidney. *J. Biophys. Biochem. Cytol.* **3,** 1037.

Straus, W. (1964). Factors affecting the state of injected horseradish peroxidase in animal tissues and procedures for the study of phagosomes and phagolysosomes. *J. Histochem. Cytochem.* **12,** 470.

Straus, W. (1969). Use of horseradish peroxidase as a marker protein for studies of phagolysosomes, permeability, and immunology. *Meth. Achievm. Exp. Path.,* **4,** 54.

Strum, J. M., and Karnovsky, M. J. (1970a). Cytochemical localization of endogenous peroxidase in thyroid follicular cells. *J. Cell Biol.* **44,** 655.

Strum, J. M., and Karnovsky, M. J. (1970b). Ultrastructural localization of peroxidase in submaxillary acinar cells. *J. Ultrastruct. Res.* **31,** 323.

Tanford, C., and Lovrien, R. (1962). Dissociation of catalase into subunits. *J. Amer. Chem. Soc.* **84,** 1892.

Threadgold, L. T., and Read, C. P. (1968). Electron microscopy of *Fasciola hepatica.* V. Peroxidase localization. *Exp. Parasit.* **23,** 221.

Todd, M. M., and Vigil, E. L. (1972). Cytochemical localization of peroxidase activity in *Saccharomyces cerevisiae. J. Histochem. Cytochem.* **20,** 344.

Tolbert, N. E., and Yamazaki, R. K. (1969). Leaf peroxisomes and their relation to photorespiration and photosynthesis. *Ann. N. Y. Acad. Sci.* **168,** 325.

van der Ploeg, M., and van Duijn, P. (1964). 5,6-Dihydroxy indole as a substrate in a histochemical peroxidase reaction. *J. Roy. Micr. Soc.* **83,** 415.

Venkatachalam, M. A., and Fahimi, H. D. (1969). The use of beef liver catalase as a protein tracer for electron microscopy. *J. Cell Biol.* **42,** 480.

Venkatachalam, M. A., Soltani, M. H., and Fahimi, H. D. (1970). The fine structural localization of peroxidase activity in the epithelium of large intestine of rat. *J. Cell Biol.* **46,** 168.

Vigil, E. L. (1970). Cytochemical and developmental changes in microbodies (glyoxysomes) and related organelles of castor bean endosperm. *J. Cell Biol.* **46,** 435.

Wood, R. L., and Legg, P. G. (1970). Peroxidase activity in rat liver micro-bodies after amino-triazole inhibition. *J. Cell Biol.* **45,** 576.

2

Acyltransferases

JOAN A. HIGGINS

*Department of Anatomy, Yale School of Medicine,
New Haven, Connecticut*

INTRODUCTION

In order for acyl fatty acids to undergo metabolic reactions, they are usually activated by the formation of their CoA derivatives (Wakil, 1970). The acyl CoA may then take part in a variety of anabolic and catabolic processes. Major among these reactions are those involving transfer of the acyl group from CoA to an acceptor molecule. These are catalyzed by a group of enzymes, the acyltransferases, which thus catalyze the general reaction:

$$\text{Acyl CoA} + \text{acceptor} \rightarrow \text{acyl acceptor} + \text{CoA}$$

where the acyl group may be any carbon chain from acetate to long-chain fatty acids, such as oleic acid, palmitic acid, or stearic acid, and where the acceptor varies dependent on the reaction catalyzed. In order to illustrate the diversity of the acyltransferases, some of these are listed in Table 2–1, together with the reaction catalyzed and its physiological significance.

Acyltransferases play important roles in a number of cellular processes, including movement of molecules across membranes, synthesis of phos-

Table 2-1   Reactions Catalyzed by Acyltransferases

Enzyme	Reaction Catalyzed	Physiological Significance
Choline acetylase	Acetyl CoA + choline → acetylcholine + CoA	Acetylcholine plays an important role as a neurotransmitter.
Carnitine acetyltransferase	Acetyl CoA + carnitine → acetylcarnitine + CoA	Involved in the movement of active acetate out of mitochondria.
Carnitine acyltransferase	Acyl CoA + carnitine → acylcarnitine + CoA	Involved in the movement of active acyl groups into mitochondria.
Acetyl CoA acetyltransferase	Acetyl CoA + acetyl CoA → acetoacetyl CoA + CoA	Regeneration of CoA for increased oxidation of fatty acids; in ketone metabolism.
Citrate synthetase	Acetyl CoA + oxalacetate → citrate + CoA	First step in Krebs cycle; oxidation of acetyl CoA.
Cholesterol esterase	Acyl CoA + cholesterol → acylcholesterol + CoA	Involved in metabolism and transport of cholesterol.
Acyl CoA monoglyceride acyltransferase	Acyl CoA + monoglyceride → diglyceride + CoA Acyl CoA + diglyceride → triglyceride + CoA	In synthesis of chylomicron triglyceride in the dietary absorption of lipid.
Acyl CoA α-glycerophosphate acyltransferases	Acyl CoA + α-glycerophosphate → lysophosphatidic acid + CoA Acyl CoA + lysophosphatidic acid → phosphatidic acid + CoA	First steps in the synthesis of triglycerides and phospholipids.

pholipids (one of the major components of membranes), synthesis of lipo-proteins involved in the transport of lipids in the plasma, and synthesis of the neurotransmitter, acetyl choline.

PRINCIPLES OF CYTOCHEMICAL REACTION

Any general method for the localization of acyltransferases must depend on the formation of an electron-dense precipitate at the site of CoA release, as this is the only product common to all the reactions catalyzed. To fulfill the requirements of the cytochemical method, the precipitant (capture reagent) used must selectively form a precipitate (reaction product) with free CoA, in the presence of acyl CoA and the acceptor used, without forming a precipitate with either of these substrates. In addition, the method must fulfill the general requirements of a cytochemical method, which are: its rapidity of formation of the precipitate; its insolubility during the fixation, dehydration, and embedding procedures; and its electron density.

The only difference between acyl CoA and free CoA is the presence of a free SH group in the latter molecule (Fig. 2–1). The cytochemical capture

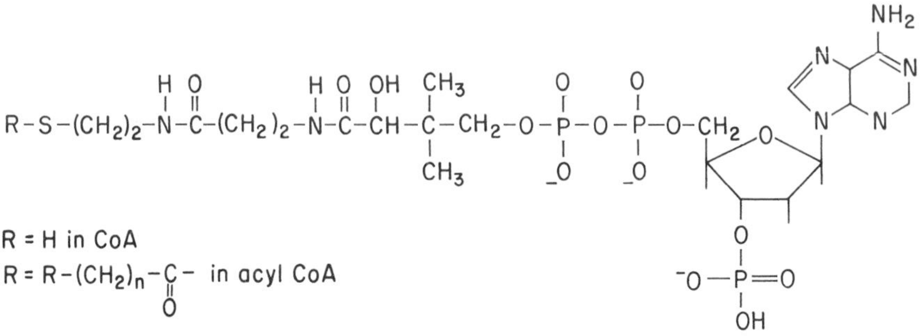

Fig. 2–1. Acyl CoA.

reagent for acyltransferases must therefore be based on this SH group, which is released through the enzymes' action. Free SH groups have two characteristics which have been exploited in the development of cytochemical methods: they form mercaptides with metal ions, and they may be oxidized to the disulfide (Higgins and Barrnett, 1970).

Cytochemical Methods Based on Mercaptide Formation

Many metals form mercaptides with SH groups. However, only a limited number of them form precipitates with free CoA without precipitating with acyl CoA (acetyl CoA and palmityl CoA have been tested). These include cadmium (Higgins and Barrnett, 1970) and lanthanum (Higgins and Barrnett, 1971), which form heavy white precipitates immediately on addition of a small amount of free CoA to a solution of cadmium nitrate or lanthanum nitrate. These therefore fulfill a second requirement of a suitable capture reagent system—the rapidity of precipitation with the product of the enzymatic activity.

The cadmium or lanthanum CoA reaction product, however, suffers from the drawback that on repeated washing of the white precipitate with buffer, it gradually dissolves, probably owing to the reversibility of the mercaptide bond. This presents a problem in the cytochemical method, as only small quantities of the precipitate form in small tissue blocks or slices, and these may be redissolved by the buffer wash, refixation in buffered osmium tetroxide, and in the first steps in the dehydration of the blocks with low concentrations of alcohol in water. In order to overcome this, use has been made of the alcoholic osmium tetroxide fixative originally described by Mizutani and Barrnett (1965) for the preservation of cadmium phosphate, a reaction product of alkaline phosphatase. Neither cadmium CoA nor lanthanum CoA dissolves in alcoholic osmium tetroxide followed by dehydration in absolute alcohol when low concentrations of alcohol in water are omitted. These precautions for the retention of the mercaptide CoA precipitate must be followed in cytochemical methods based on this principle.

Cytochemical Methods Based on the Oxidation of Free CoA

CoA is readily oxidized by potassium ferricyanide, which, in turn, is reduced to potassium ferrocyanide. The probable reactions involved are:

$$2CoA \, SH \rightarrow CoA—S—S—AoC + 2H^+ + 2e$$
$$2e + 2K_3Fe(CN)_6 \rightarrow 2K_4Fe(CN)_6$$

This reaction occurs extremely rapidly on addition of CoA to a solution of potassium ferricyanide. This reaction can be measured quantitatively by spectrophotometric assay of potassium ferrocyanide in the presence of potassium ferricyanide at 237 mμ, at which wavelength absorption is proportional to the ferrocyanide concentration (Kidby, 1969) or qualitatively by observing the disappearance of the yellow color of potassium ferricyanide.

Cytochemical methods based on the oxidation of CoA are indirect in that they involve the formation of a precipitate at the site of ferrocyanide production rather than at the site of CoA release. The oxidation reaction is, however, sufficiently rapid that these two points are probably indistinguishable in terms of the resolution of the electron microscope. This method, however, has additional requirements over those of the direct methods based on mercaptide formation. Thus, it is necessary to develop conditions which favor the reduction of ferricyanide by free CoA and in which the precipitation of ferrocyanide occurs without precipitation of either ferricyanide or the substrates used for the enzymic reaction.

Three methods have been developed for the localization of acyltransferases based on the oxidation of CoA by ferricyanide. Each of these has specific problems, and will be considered individually.

Copper-ferrocyanide method. This method was originally developed by Karnovsky and Roots (1964) for the localization of acetylcholinesterase using acetylthiocholine as a substrate, which yields thiocholine on hydrolysis. The method was modified for the localization of acyltransferase (Benes *et al.,* 1972). Under the conditions used, cupric ions form a precipitate with ferricyanide, and therefore these are chelated with either citrate or tartarate in the incubation medium. Ferrocyanide has a greater affinity for cupric ions than the chelating agent, and on reduction of the ferricyanide, a precipitate of cupric-ferrocyanide forms. This reaction product forms most readily at pH's below 6.6, although it has been used with success at as high as pH 7.4 (Benes *et al.,* 1972). Above this pH, however, formation of a precipitate in the presence of free CoA may be sufficiently slow to cause diffusion artifacts.

Uranyl-ferrocyanide method. In this method, uranyl acetate is used as a precipitant for ferrocyanide (Higgins and Barrnett, 1970). This does not precipitate with ferricyanide, and therefore no chelating agent is used. As with the cupric-ferrocyanide method, uranyl-ferrocyanide forms most rapidly at pH's below 6.6, although it has been used successfully at pH 7.0.

Manganous-ferrocyanide method. Manganous chloride forms a white precipitate with potassium ferrocyanide at all pH's studied (from 6.6 to 7.7), while no precipitate forms with potassium ferricyanide (Higgins and Barrnett, 1971). The only apparent complication of this method for localization of acyltransferases is the fact that palmityl CoA tends to form precipitates with manganous chloride at concentrations of the former above 200 μ molarity. This does not occur with acetyl CoA. Therefore the selection of the final concentration of manganous chloride for a cytochemical method will depend upon the enzyme under investigation.

Apart from the individual characteristics of the three methods indicated above, cupric-ferrocyanide, uranyl-ferrocyanide, and manganous-ferrocyanide are not solublized by the fixation, dehydration, and embedding procedures used in the preparation of tissue blocks for electron microscopy. All three reaction products form satisfactory electron-dense deposits, although, in the case of manganous-ferrocyanide, these tend to be somewhat delicate.

GENERAL PROCEDURES AND CONTROL EXPERIMENTS

Biochemical Controls

As most cytochemical experiments minimally involve the incubation of tissue samples in media, which may contain potential enzyme inhibitors, it is always advisable to perform biochemical assays of the enzymes under investigation as a preliminary to cytochemical experiments. This is especially true in the case of the acyltransferases, which are susceptible to inhibition by heavy metal ions. It is also usually necessary to preserve tissue morphology during the cytochemical experiment by fixation, which may also inhibit the enzymes. In preliminary biochemical experiments, it is therefore suggested that: the specific activity of the enzyme under investigation in homogenates of unfixed tissue be determined and compared with the activity in homogenates of fixed tissue; the rate of the enzymic reaction in slices of fixed tissue be compared with that of homogenates of fixed tissue; and the effect of the capture reagents on the enzymic activity in slices of fixed tissue be measured. With this data, it should be possible to state: the effect of the fixation process on the enzyme under investigation; the existence of barriers to penetration of substrates in slices of fixed tissue compared with homogenates in which these barriers are broken down; and the effect, if any, of capture reagents on the enzyme under investigation.

In order to illustrate the value of such control studies, some results of biochemical experiments of the acyltransferases involved in the synthesis of phospholipid in rat liver are indicated below. These enzymes catalyze the reactions

palmityl CoA + α-glycerophosphate → lysophosphatidic acid + CoA
palmityl CoA + lysophosphatidic acid → phosphatidic acid + CoA

and are therefore assayed by measurement of the incorporation of ^{14}C-α-glycerophosphate into phosphatidic acid (Higgins and Barrnett, 1972).

Effect of fixation. The effect of fixation by perfusion with 0.5% glutaraldehyde in cacodylate buffer, 0.05M, pH 7.4, containing 4.5% dextrose, on the acyltransferase activity of rat liver is shown in Fig. 2–2a. The fixation procedure inhibits the enzyme system by 70 to 75%. This level of inhibition was found consistently in liver when the tissue was sliced 1 to 2 mm thick after perfusion and washed in the buffer of perfusion for 2 hr. If, however, the tissue was washed for longer periods, 15 to 18 hr, after fixation there was greater loss of activity. A short washing after mild fixation is therefore critical in the investigation of these enzymes.

In liver, formaldehyde was found to completely inhibit acyltransferase activity. On the other hand, the same enzyme in rabbit and rat lung (Page-Roberts, personal communication), in the trigeminal nerve of the developing rat (Benes, Higgins, and Barrnett, 1973), and in the salt gland of the domestic duckling (Levine *et al.,* 1972) was found to survive fixation in mixtures of 1.0% formaldehyde (freshly prepared from paraformaldehyde) and 0.25% glutaraldehyde at levels of up to 50% of the activity of unfixed tissue. The use of mixtures of formaldehyde and glutaraldehyde may therefore be preferable for the investigation of acyltransferases in some tissues, and for this reason assay of the enzymes after fixation is strongly recommended.

In general, it has been found that all acyltransferases studied are inhibited to some extent by the available fixatives, formaldehyde and glutaraldehyde, used either separately or in a mixture. However, fixation appears to be necessary, both to preserve the tissue morphology during the fairly long cytochemical incubations and to break down permeability bar-

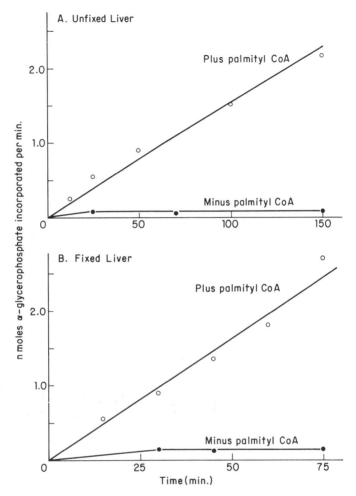

Fig. 2–2a. Incorporation of α-glycerophosphate into lipids of fixed and unfixed rat liver. Homogenates of unfixed and fixed rat liver were incubated in media containing α-glycerophosphate (1.8 mM) with or without palmityl CoA (0.2 mM) in caco-dylate buffer, pH 7.2, 0.05 M containing 4.5% dextrose (final volume 1.0 ml) at 37° for a range of times (0 to 30 min). At the end of the incubation period, the reaction was stopped by addition of ice-cold chloroform methanol (2/1) and the lipid extracted and counted. The initial rate of incorporation of ^{14}C α-glycerophosphate is plotted against concentration of liver. In (a), unfixed liver was used; in (b), liver was fixed by perfusion with 0.5% glutaraldehyde (from Higgins and Barrnett, 1972).

riers which may exist in the unfixed tissue against both the substrates and the capture reagents. It may therefore be necessary to compromise be-tween an acceptable preservation of morphology and retention of enzymic activity. This compromise should be made on the basis of the objectives

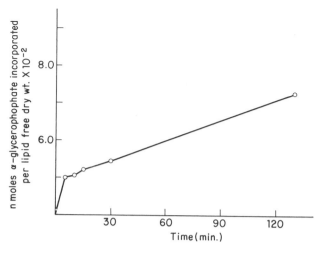

Fig. 2–2b. Incorporation of ^{14}C α-glycerophosphate into lipid by slices of fixed liver. Slices of liver were incubated in media containing α-glycerophosphate (1.8 mM) and palmityl CoA (0.2 mM) in cacodylate buffer pH 7.2 (0.05 M) containing 4.5% dextrose at 37° for a range of times. The reaction was stopped by addition of ice-cold chloroform/methanol (2/1), and the lipid extracted and counted. Incorporation of α-glycerophosphate into lipid per mg of lipid-free dry weight is plotted against time of incubation (from Higgins and Barrnett, 1972).

of individual investigations. This subject has been discussed in detail by Hayat (1970 and 1973).

Rate of reaction. The time course of incorporation of α-glycerophosphate into phosphatidic acid by slices of fixed liver is shown in Fig. 2–2b. Homogenates of the same tissue show an extremely rapid incorporation, which reaches a plateau after 10 min. The rate of incorporation is considerably slower in the former, indicating a retarded penetration of one or more of the substrates. For this reason, tissue sections cut as thin as possible with a McIllwain or Smith-Farquhar tissue chopper should be used in order to facilitate penetration of substrates. In addition, long incubation times of 1 to 2 hr may be required in order to obtain a satisfactory accumulation of reaction product.

Effects of capture reagents. The effects of the copper-ferrocyanide and the manganous-ferrocyanide capture reagent system on the incorporation of α-glycerophosphate into phosphatidic acid are shown in Table 2–2. The manganous-ferrocyanide reagents have no effect on the reaction, while the copper-ferrocyanide reagents inhibit the enzyme system by approximately 50%.

Table 2–2   Effect of Capture Reagents on the Incorporation of
^{14}C α-glycerophosphate into Esterified Lipid of Slices of Fixed
Rat Liver

	Incubation Conditions	nmoles of ^{14}C α-Glycerophosphate Incorporated per mg Lipid-Free Dry Weight
Experiment 1		
	Control	4.70
	plus copper-ferrocyanide capture reagents	2.70
Experiment 2		
	Control	3.71
	plus manganous-ferrocyanide capture reagents	4.46

Slices of fixed liver were incubated in media containing ^{14}C α-glycerophosphate and palmityl CoA for 60 min in the presence or absence of capture reagents (see the section on localization of acyltransferase). The lipid was extracted, and the incorporation of ^{14}C into lipid per mg of lipid-free dry weight determined (from Higgins and Barrnett, 1972; Benes, Higgins, and Barrnett, 1972).

In other tissues, and with other acyltransferases investigated, the manganous-ferrocyanide reagents were found to have no effect on the enzymic activity; investigations of the mercaptide-forming capture reagents indicated that these tended to be somewhat inhibitory at the concentrations used for cytochemical methods.

Hydrolysis of acyl CoA. The use of labeled palmityl CoA together with unlabeled α-glycerophosphate indicated that even in fixed liver there is a fairly active palmityl CoA hydrolase (Benes *et al.,* 1972). This is partly inhibited by preincubation of tissue slices with 10^{-3} M di-isopropyl-fluorophosphate (DFP) (Lands and Hart, 1965), although 100% inhibition cannot be achieved using this inhibitor.

In other tissues, the palmityl CoA hydrolase, although present, is considerably less active than in the liver. However, in all cases, hydrolysis of palmityl CoA, yielding CoA, which might potentially form reaction product, presents a problem in the interpretation of the results of acyltransferase localization experiments. This therefore necessitates the use of cytochemical controls, which are indicated in the next section.

Cytochemical Controls

Basic controls. Having established from the biochemical assays the most appropriate fixation procedure and capture reagent system for the acyltransferase under investigation, there are additional basic controls for the cytochemical methods. Thus, the following incubations should be minimally performed: (a) the complete medium containing acyl CoA, acceptor, and capture reagents; (b) no acyl CoA control containing acceptor and capture reagents; (c) no acceptor control containing acyl CoA and capture reagents; (d) no substrate control containing capture reagents. In addition, if the investigator is not familiar with the morphology of the tissue under investigation and the possible existence of endogenous electron-dense deposits, it is also necessary to incubate the tissue in the absence of both substrates and capture reagents.

With these basic controls, it should be possible to distinguish reaction product formed as a result of acyltransferase activity from that due to hydrolysis of palmityl CoA or the acceptor. For example, α-glycerophosphate may be hydrolyzed by acid phosphatase and, in the presence of a suitable heavy metal, the released phosphate may be precipitated as an electron-dense deposit, which would complicate the reaction for the acyltransferase. Such a possibility would be indicated by the control (b) above. Likewise, deposits due to hydrolysis of palmityl CoA would be indicated by control (c), and reactions due to the capture reagents alone would be indicated by control (d). Additional controls dependent on the enzyme and the cytochemical method selected may also be necessary.

Preoxidation controls. In the cytochemical methods based on the oxidation of CoA by ferricyanide, early studies indicated the formation of reaction product, restricted to the mitochondria, in tissues incubated in media containing only capture reagents (Higgins and Barrnett, 1970). This was attributed to the presence of endogenous electron donors, and was eliminated by preincubation of the tissue in potassium ferricyanide at the same or double the concentration used for the cytochemical experiments. The preoxidation step is therefore used routinely in cytochemical methods for the localization of acyltransferases based on the oxidation of ferricyanide.

Inhibitor controls. The formation of reaction product in cytochemical experiments is often subject to criticisms as to the specificity of the reaction catalyzed. The use of the controls indicated above should at least indicate a requirement of the cytochemical reaction for substrates and, together with the biochemical analysis, provide strong evidence of the enzymic activity involved. This may be further substantiated by the use of inhibitors. If a specific inhibitor of the enzyme under investigation is available, additional tissue specimens should be incubated in the complete experimental medium containing the inhibitor. Unfortunately, such specific inhibitors are not available for many acyltransferases; however, as these are in general sulfhydryl-dependent enzymes, nonspecific inhibitors which bind to sulfhydryl groups may be used. These include p chloromercuribenzoate, mercuric chloride, and N ethylmaleimide. A survey of the literature will indicate the inhibitor and the concentration most suitable for the enzyme under investigation. Tissue blocks may also be heated at sufficiently high temperature to destroy enzymic activity without extensive destruction of structure, for example, at 60° for several hours. The use of the various inhibitors as controls will depend on the enzyme, the results of the basic cytochemical controls, and the availability of suitable inhibitors.

SPECIFIC PROCEDURES

The above reactions concerned with general procedures for the localization of acyltransferases may be applied to the investigation of any of this group of enzymes. In this section, specific procedures which have been successfully applied to some of these enzymes will be detailed.

Carnitine Acetyltransferase

Carnitine acetyltransferase catalyzes the reaction

$$carnitine + acetyl\ CoA \rightarrow acetylcarnitine + CoA$$

and plays an important role in the movement of "active acetate" from the mitochondria, where it is synthesized, to the cytoplasm, where it is used in a variety of biosynthetic processes (Bremer, 1962; Fritz and Yue, 1964; Bressler and Brendel, 1966). This enzyme has been localized at the fine structural level by the mercaptide method, using cadmium as a capture reagent, and by the uranyl-ferrocyanide method (Higgins and Barrnett, 1970).

Tissue preparation. Rat heart was the tissue used in the method reported for localization of carnitine acetyltransferase, as this tissue has the highest level of this enzyme (Marquis and Fritz, 1965). This is a fairly "hardy" tissue, and may be incubated without severe loss of morphological integrity. If less "hardy" tissues are investigated, or if good preservation of fine structure is required, the tissues may be fixed either by immersion for 10 to 15 min or by perfusion for a similar period in a mixture of 1.0% formaldehyde (freshly prepared from paraformaldehyde) and 0.25% glutaraldehyde, in cacodylate buffer, 0.05 M, adjusted to pH 7.4 with nitric acid and containing 4.5% dextrose. The fixed tissue is then sliced and washed in the buffer of the perfusion for periods of up to 18 hr.

Cadmium method.

Incubation Medium

Cadmium nitrate 4H$_2$O	4.0 mg/ml
Acetyl CoA	0.8 mg/ml (Sigma Chemical Co.)
Carnitine	1.6 mg/ml (Sigma Chemical Co.)

The above reagents were dissolved in cacodylate buffer, 0.05 M, adjusted to pH 7.0 with nitric acid and containing 4.5% dextrose. This buffer was used throughout.

The procedure was as follows: unfixed or fixed chopper sections of heart were incubated in the above media and in suitable control media, as indicated earlier, for 30 to 60 min at room temperature. At the end of the incubation, the unfixed sections were fixed by immersion for 30 min in 3% glutaraldehyde in buffer (pH 7.4) containing cadmium nitrate (4 mg/ml), which was included in the fixative in order to preserve the cadmium CoA precipitate, which is removed by washing in the absence of excess cadmium ions. All blocks fixed before or after incubation were refixed, without washing, in alcoholic osmium tetroxide prepared immediately before use by mixing a 4% aqueous solution of osmium tetroxide with cacodylate buffer (pH 7.4) and absolute ethanol in the ratio 1:1:2 (Mizutani and Barrnett, 1965). The time of refixation was dependent on the stability of the fixative, which tends to blacken and form a precipitate within 30 min of preparation. After refixation, the sections were dehydrated through several changes of absolute alcohol followed by propylene oxide and embedded in Epon-Araldite. The procedures, by steps, for embedding have been presented by Hayat (1972).

Uranyl-ferrocyanide method.

Incubation Medium

Potassium ferricyanide	2.0 mg/ml
Uranyl acetate	1.0 mg/ml
Acetyl CoA	0.8 mg/ml
Carnitine	1.6 mg/ml

These were dissolved in cacodylate buffer, pH 7.0, as for the cadmium method.

The procedure was as follows: As a routine step before incubation, all tissue sections were incubated for 30 min in media containing potassium ferricyanide (2.0 mg/ml) in cacodylate buffer (pH 7.0) to preoxidize endogenous reducing material. The tissue blocks were rinsed with several changes of buffer and incubated in the above medium and in appropriate control media for 30 to 60 min. At the end of the incubation period, the unfixed blocks were fixed in 3% glutaraldehyde in cacodylate buffer (pH 7.4). All blocks were then refixed in 1% osmium tetroxide in cacodylate buffer (pH 7.4) for 30 to 60 min, dehydrated through a graded series of solutions of ethyl alcohol, propylene oxide, and embedded in Epon or Epon-Araldite. Thin sections were cut from the tissue close to the edge of the block, where maximum penetration of substrates and reagents occurred, and poststained with lead citrate.

Observations. Heart muscle sections incubated in the complete medium for carnitine acetyltransferase by the uranyl-ferrocyanide method are illustrated in Figs. 2–3 and 2–4. In tissues incubated either fixed or unfixed,

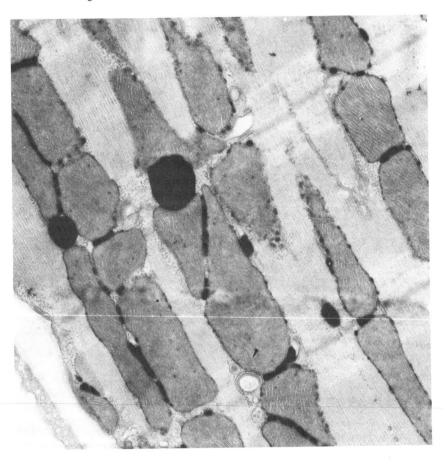

Fig. 2–3. Fixed rat heart incubated in the complete medium for localization of carnitine acetyltransferase by the uranyl-ferrocyanide method. Note reaction product between the inner and outer mitochondrial membranes. ×28,000.

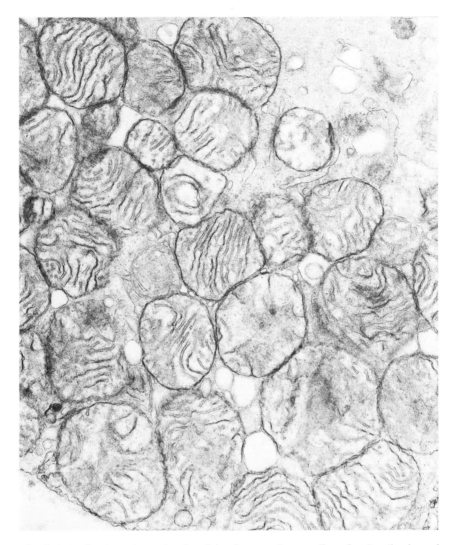

Fig. 2–4. Unfixed rat heart incubated in the complete medium for localization of acyltransferase by the uranyl-ferrocyanide method. Note reaction product between the inner and outer mitochondrial membrane and in the intracristal space. ×22,000.

reaction product is restricted to the mitochondria; in fixed tissues, it is restricted to the space between the inner and outer membranes. In unfixed tissues, reaction product occurs, in addition, in the intracristal space. When acetyl CoA is omitted from the incubation medium, the reaction product is absent from both fixed and unfixed tissues. If, however, carnitine is omitted from the incubation medium, reaction product in the unfixed tis-

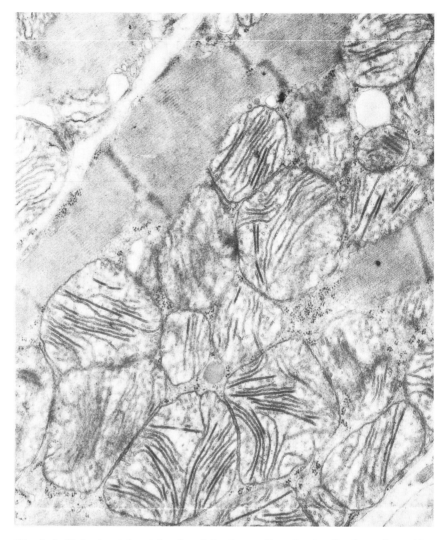

Fig. 2–5. Unfixed rat heart incubated in the medium for localization of carnitine acetyltransferase by the uranyl-ferrocyanide method omitting carnitine. Note reaction product in intracristal space, but absent from between the inner and outer mitochondrial membranes. X22,000.

sue is absent from the site between the inner and outer membranes, but is retained in the intracristal space (Fig. 2–5).

These results suggest that the enzymic activity resulting in the deposition of reaction product in the intracristal space is due not to carnitine acetyltransferase but to an enzyme requiring only acetyl CoA. This may be acetyl CoA hydrolase, or it may be due to some other transferase the acceptor of which is present in sufficient quantities to allow the reaction to proceed. Carnitine acetyltransferase appears to be located in such a way that CoA produced through its action is released on either the inner surface of the outer membrane or the outer surface of the inner membrane.

Carnitine acetyltransferase is inhibited by sulfhydryl inhibitors and by acetylcarnitine (Fritz and Schultz, 1965). The latter is a specific inhibitor for the enzyme, but acts as a competitive inhibitor and therefore must be used in extremely high concentrations. Inclusion of mercuric acetate (4×10^{-4} M) as a sulfhydryl inhibitor in the complete experimental incubation medium resulted in absence of reaction product from all sites in both fixed and unfixed tissue, while acetylcarnitine at a concentration of 3.2 mg/ml, which resulted in loss of 80% of the enzyme activity, caused a severe reduction of the reaction product in the fixed tissue. In the unfixed tissue, the high concentration of acetyl carnitine caused such severe structural changes that its use was not possible.

In using the cadmium method for the localization of carnitine acetyltransferase, a similar deposition of reaction product was found (Fig. 2–6). The tissue, however, was considerably less well preserved, presumably because of the use of alcoholic osmium tetroxide as a fixative. The reaction product formed in this case was less discrete than that yielded by uranyl ferrocyanide in that ferrocyanide had a diffuse appearance. For these reasons, this method is less satisfactory than the uranyl-ferrocyanide method, which is the method of choice for this enzyme.

Localization of carnitine acetyltransferase by cell fractionation procedures. Carnitine acetyltransferase has been found, in a number of tissues, to be restricted to the mitochondria (Marquis and Fritz, 1965), a location consistent with the cytochemical findings. On separation of the inner and outer mitochondrial membranes, the enzyme was found to be associated with the former fraction (Norum *et al.,* 1966). If this is correct, the cytochemical findings suggest that the enzyme is located in such a manner that the CoA is released at the outer surface of the inner membrane. A release of acetylcarnitine at this site would also be consistent with the suggested function of the enzyme, i.e., in the movement of acetylcarnitine from the mitochondria to the cytoplasm (Wakil, 1970).

Acyltransferase Involved in the Acylation of Monoglyceride

A pathway in intestinal mucosa for the synthesis of triglyceride by acylation of monoglyceride has been reported (Clark and Hubscher, 1961). The reactions catalyzed are

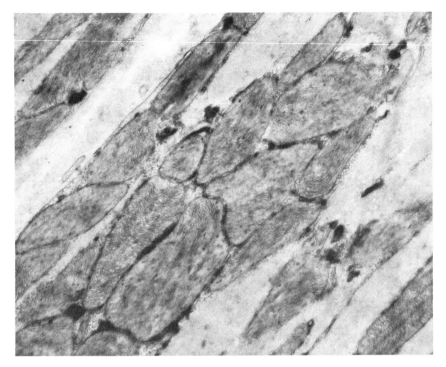

Fig. 2–6. Unfixed rat heart incubated in the complete medium for the localization of carnitine acetyltransferase by the cadmium method. Reaction product is restricted mainly to the space between the inner and outer mitochondrial membranes, although this is less sharply defined than in the uranyl-ferrocyanide method. X21,000.

$$\text{acyl CoA} + \text{monoglyceride} \rightarrow \text{diglyceride} + \text{CoA}$$
$$\text{acyl CoA} + \text{diglyceride} \rightarrow \text{triglyceride} + \text{CoA}$$

where the acyl CoA may be any long chain fatty acid. In the present study, palmityl CoA was used.

These two steps are catalyzed by acyltransferases, which are believed to be part of a single enzyme complex (Rao and Johnston, 1966), in such a manner that the localization of one enzyme is the same as the localization of the whole complex.

These acyltransferases have been localized at the fine structural level by the mercaptide method, using lanthanum as a capture reagent, and by the manganous-ferrocyanide method.

Tissue preparation. Fixed tissue has been used for the most satisfactory localization in this case, as unfixed intestinal mucosa is not satisfactorily preserved during the incubation procedure. Intestine from the duodenum and the upper part of the jejumum was taken from a rat, starved for 48 hr prior to sacrifice, and the mucosa fixed by lavage of the lumen with 1% glutaraldehyde in 0.05 M cacodylate buffer adjusted to pH 7.4 with nitric acid and containing 4.5% dextrose. The intestine was cut into rings and immersed in the same fixative for an additional 15 min. The rings were then washed in the buffer of fixation for 2 to 18 hr before cytochemical experiments.

Assay of the enzymic activity of intestinal rings indicated that esterification of monoglyceride was the same in both unfixed and fixed tissue. However, accumulation of diglyceride occurred in fixed tissue, while the reaction proceeded to triglyceride in unfixed tissue, suggesting that the second acylation step was inhibited by fixation to a greater extent than was the first.

Lanthanum method.

Incubation Medium

Lanthanum nitrate 6 H_2O	1.0 mg/ml	
Palmityl CoA	0.2 mg/ml	freshly weighed out prior to preparation of medium
Monopalmitin	0.25 mg/ml	prepared in stock of 2.5 mg/ml by sonication in distilled water

This was dissolved in cacodylate buffer, pH 7.0, as in the previous method.

The procedure was as follows: Rings of intestine were incubated in the complete medium indicated above and in appropriate control media for 1 to 2 hr at room temperature. The rings were removed from the incubation media and immediately refixed in alcoholic osmium tetroxide prepared as described above. These were then dehydrated with absolute ethanol and propylene oxide, cut into pieces, and embedded in Epon. The pieces were oriented using a dissecting microscope so that the microvilli were toward the block surface and hence sectioned before the muscle layers of the intestine.

Manganous-ferrocyanide method.

Incubation Medium

Manganous chloride 4 H_2O	0.5 mg/ml
Potassium ferricyanide	0.15 mg/ml

| Palmityl CoA | 0.2 mg/ml | freshly weighed out prior to preparation of medium |
| Monopalmitin | 0.25 mg/ml | prepared, as a stock, as above |

This was dissolved in cacodylate buffer pH 7.0, as above.

The procedure was as follows: Rings of intestine were preincubated for 30 min in potassium ferricyanide (0.3 mg/ml) in cacodylate buffer to oxidize endogenous reducing material. The rings were then rinsed in several changes of buffer and incubated in the above medium and in appropriate control media for 1 to 2 hr. The rings were rinsed in several changes of buffer and refixed in 1% osmium tetroxide in cacodylate buffer (pH 7.4) for 30 to 60 min, dehydrated through a graded series of solutions of ethanol, followed by propylene oxide, and embedded in Epon. Blocks were oriented as for the lanthanum method.

Observations. As in the case of carnitine acetyltransferase localization, the results with the manganous-ferrocyanide method, with regard to both the tissue morphology and the quality of reaction product, were superior to those with the mercaptide method.

With the lanthanum method, sections of control tissues incubated in media containing only capture reagents showed deposits of lanthanum associated with the surface of the brush border and with the intercellular space. This has been reported elsewhere, and is believed to be due to staining of the mucopolysaccharide of the surface coats (Overton, 1967). Blocks of tissue incubated in the complete medium showed reaction product, in addition, within the smooth endoplasmic reticulum at the apex of the absorptive cells. This reaction product appeared to fill the cisternae rather than to be associated with the membranes (Fig. 2–7).

Tissue incubated in the complete medium for localization of acyltransferases by the manganous-ferrocyanide method showed reaction product associated with the smooth endoplasmic reticulum at the apex of the mucosal cells (Figs. 2–8 and 2–9). This was more discrete than the reaction product in the lanthanum method, and was absent when either monopalmitin or palmityl CoA was omitted from the incubation medium.

Localization of monoglyceride acylating enzymes by cell fractionation techniques. The enzymes involved in the monoglyceride pathway for the synthesis of triglyceride have been found to be associated with the microsomal fraction of the intestinal mucosa (Brindley and Hubscher, 1965). This is consistent with the cytochemical observations. On separation of

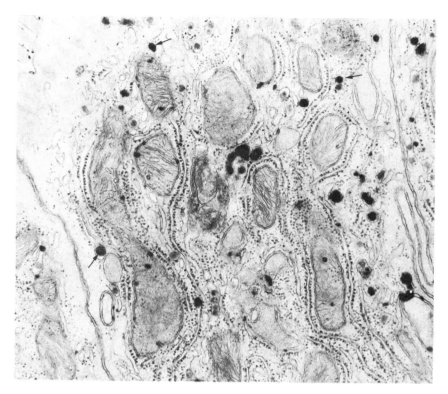

Fig. 2–7. Apical region of intestinal absorptive cell, from fasted rat intestine fixed by immersion in 0.5% glutaraldehyde, incubated in the complete medium for localization of acyltransferases involved in acylation of monoglycerides by the lanthanum method. Note reaction product filling the cisternae of smooth endoplasmic reticulum. Lanthanum also tends to adhere to the surface of brush border. X37,000.

the rough and smooth microsomes, however, these enzymes were found to be associated with the rough microsomes and to a lesser extent with a subfraction of smooth microsomes (Brindley and Hubscher, 1965). This is in conflict with the cytochemical observations that the monoglyceride pathway acyltransferases are located in the smooth endoplasmic reticulum. There are difficulties, however, in preparing pure fractions of smooth and rough microsomes, especially in separating these two forms of membranes at the site of their continuity, where the acyltransferases appear to be located. This may account for the conflict between these results. The cytochemical observations are consistent with the morphological observations during lipid absorption, when the apparent triglyceride droplets first appear within the smooth endoplasmic reticular cisternae at a similar site to the acyltransferase localization (Cardell et al., 1967).

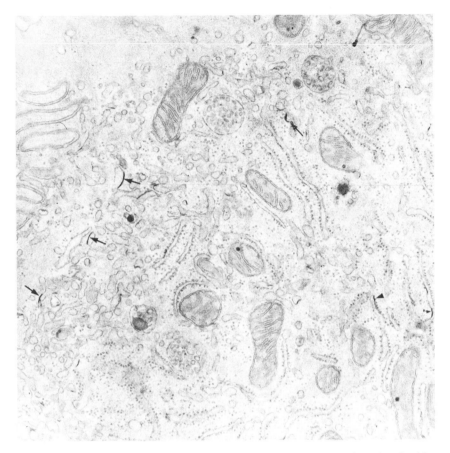

Fig. 2–8. Apical region of intestinal absorptive cell, from fasted rat intestine fixed by immersion in 0.5% glutaraldehyde, incubated in the complete medium for the localization of the acyltransferases involved in acylation of monoglyceride, by the manganous-ferrocyanide method. Note reaction product (arrows) associated with smooth endoplasmic reticulum and to a lesser extent with the rough endoplasmic reticulum (arrow heads). X30,000.

Acyltransferases Involved in the Acylation of α-Glycerophosphate

The major pathways for the synthesis of phospholipids and for triglycerides in many tissues involve acylation of α-glycerophosphate by the following reactions:

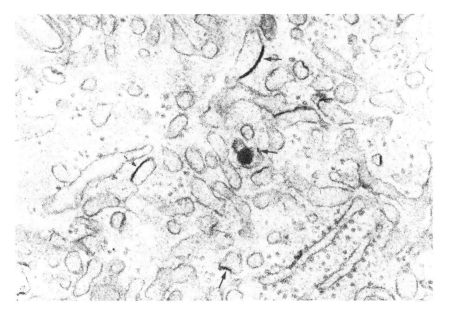

Fig. 2–9. As Fig. 2–8. ×80,000.

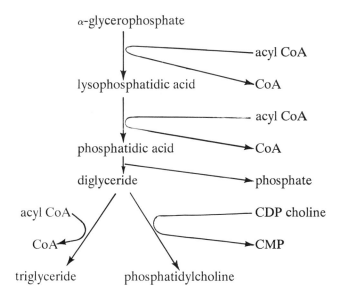

It should be noted that the above scheme is one pathway for the synthesis of phosphatidylcholine. Alternative pathways exist for synthesis of phosphotidylcholine and for other glycerophospholipids; however, these all have in common the first steps in which acylation of α-glycerophosphate occurs.

Tissue preparation. Acyltransferases involved in acylation of α-glycerophosphate have been localized in liver (Higgins and Barrnett, 1972; Benes *et al.,* 1972), intestine (Higgins and Barrnett, 1971), and the trigeminal nerve (Benes, Higgins and Barrnett, 1973). The cytochemical methods used in all cases are basically the same, although, as indicated earlier, differences between the susceptibility of the enzymes to fixation have been found between tissues. The fixation procedure should therefore be selected on the basis of biochemical controls. For the purpose of this account, the methods applied to liver will be detailed.

Liver was fixed by perfusion of the whole animal with 0.5% glutaraldehyde in cacodylate buffer, 0.05 M, pH 7.4, containing 4.5% dextrose. The tissue was removed, sliced 1 to 2 mm thick, and washed in the buffer of fixation for 2 hr. Thin chopper sections, ~100 μ thick, were cut and incubated in the cytochemical experiments.

Manganous-ferrocyanide method.

Incubation Medium

Manganous chloride 4 H_2O	0.5 mg/ml	
Potassium ferricyanide	0.15 mg/ml	
Palmityl CoA	0.1 mg/ml	weighed out immediately prior to preparation of medium
α-glycerophosphate	0.5 mg/ml	

This was dissolved in cacodylate buffer, pH 7.0 as above.

Copper-ferrocyanide method. This medium is prepared by mixing freshly prepared stock solutions in the order indicated:

0.05 M sodium hydrogen maleate buffer pH 7.0	6.5 ml
0.05 M sodium citrate 2 H_2O	0.5 ml
0.03 M cupric sulfate	1.0 ml
distilled water	1.0 ml
0.005 M potassium ferricyanide	1.0 ml
palmityl CoA to give a final concentration of 0.1 mg/ml	
α-glycerophosphate to give a final concentration of 0.5 mg/ml	

The procedure was as follows: Except for the buffer wash, which was the same as that of the incubation medium, the same procedure was used for both methods. Sections of liver were preincubated in potassium ferri-cyanide (0.3 mg/ml in buffer) for 30 min, rinsed with several changes of buffer, and incubated in the complete medium and in appropriate control media for 1 to 2 hr. The sections were rinsed with buffer and refixed in 1% buffered osmium tetroxide for 30 to 60 min, followed by dehydration through a graded series of ethanol, propylene oxide, and embedded in Epon (Hayat, 1972).

Observations. Reaction product is associated with the rough and smooth endoplasmic reticulum in both methods. This is absent from tissues in-cubated either with palmityl CoA alone or with α-glycerophosphate alone. The reaction product in the copper method is electron-dense, and tends to form heavy deposits filling the cisternae (Fig. 2–10), while that of the manganous method is less heavy, and tends to line the inner surface of the membrane of the rough endoplasmic reticulum and to form laminated

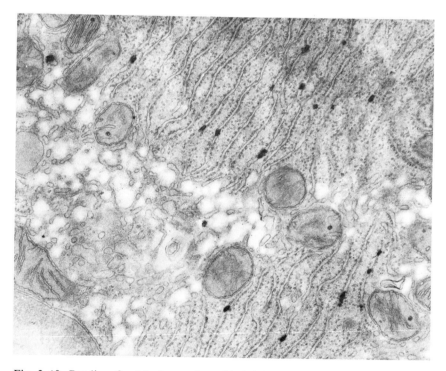

Fig. 2–10. Rat liver fixed by immersion with 0.5% glutaraldehyde and incubated in the complete medium for the localization of the acyltransferases involved in the acyla-tion of α-glycerophosphate by the copper-ferrocyanide method. Note reaction product as heavy deposits within the cisternal space of both the rough and smooth endoplasmic reticulum. X50,000.

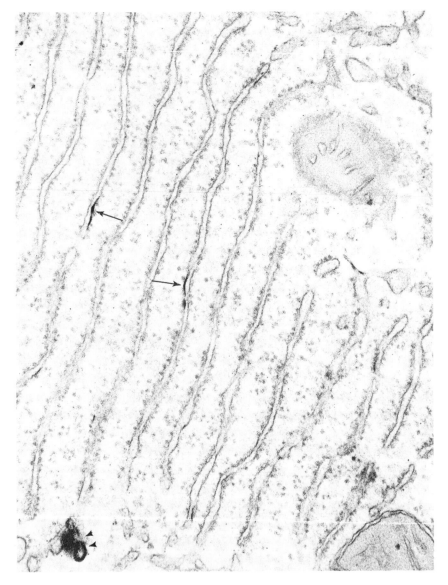

Fig. 2–11. Rat liver fixed by perfusion with 0.5% glutaraldehyde and incubated in the complete medium for localization of acyltransferases involved in acylation of α-gly-cerophosphate by the manganous-ferrocyanide method. Note delicate deposits of reaction product lining inner surface of rough endoplasmic reticulum (arrows) and tending to form laminated deposits in the smooth endoplasmic reticulum (arrow heads).

deposits in association with the smooth endoplasmic reticulum (Figs. 2–11 and 2–12). Such laminated deposits are characteristic of this reaction product, and may possibly be related to the crystal structure of the precipitate.

Localization of the α-glycerophosphate acylating enzymes by cell-fractionation techniques. The acyltransferases of this pathway have been studied extensively in liver, and have been found to be restricted to the microsome fraction, which is consistent with the cytochemical findings (Eibl *et al.,* 1969). In the normal liver, on separation of the rough and smooth microsomes, the specific activity of the acyltransferases of the former is slightly higher than that of the latter (Higgins and Barrnett, 1972). This is also consistent with the cytochemical findings, which, although more difficult to quantitate, do show greater deposition of reaction product in the rough endoplasmic reticulum than in the smooth.

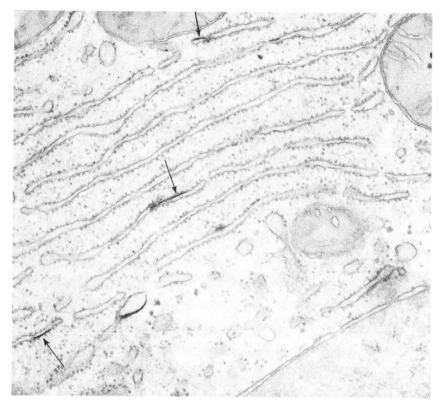

Fig. 2–12. As Fig. 2–11. X30,000.

APPLICATION TO SPECIFIC PROBLEMS

The most valuable contribution of cytochemical methods for the localization of acyltransferases has been to an understanding of the organization of the cell in lipid metabolism. Some applications of these methods to specific cell biological problems will be briefly described here.

Intestinal Lipid Absorption

During lipid absorption from the intestine, interluminal hydrolysis of dietary triglyceride by pancreatic lipase yields mainly monoglyceride and free fatty acids, which are absorbed across the brush border. Inside the cell, the fatty acids are reactivated by synthesis of their CoA derivatives, and triglycerides and phospholipids are resynthesized and packaged with cholesterol, cholesterol esters, and a small amount of protein to yield chylomicrons, which are released from the cell into the intercellular spaces, from which they drain into the lymph (Hubscher, *et al.,* 1963; Johnston, 1968; Senior, 1964).

The existence in intestinal mucosal cells of two pathways for the synthesis of triglyceride from fatty acyl CoA has been established. One pathway uses the absorbed monoglyceride as an acceptor for the fatty acid to yield triglyceride by the pathway indicated earlier (Clark and Hubscher, 1961; Johnston and Brown, 1962), while the second uses α-glycerophosphate as an acceptor (Dawson and Isselbacher, 1960a, 1960b; Johnston, 1959). During lipid absorption, the monoglyceride pathway is used preferentially for the synthesis of triglyceride, and the α-glycerophosphate pathway for the synthesis of phospholipid (Kern and Borgstrom, 1965).

Cytochemical experiments for the localization of the acyltransferases of the monoglyceride pathway indicated that these are associated with the smooth endoplasmic reticulum and also with the outer elements of the Golgi membranes. Similar experiments to investigate the site of acyltransferases of the α-glycerophosphate pathway indicated that these are associated with the rough endoplasmic reticular membranes and with the outer elements of the Golgi region (Higgins and Barrnett, 1971). These observations clearly demonstrate a morphological sequestration of the two pathways involved in synthesis of the major components of chylomicrons. Some form of sequestration, in which diglyceride of one pathway is not available for the other pathway, has been suggested by biochemical observations (Johnston *et al.,* 1967).

In view of the cytochemical observations coupled with biochemical results, the following organization of the intestinal cell in the synthesis of chylomicrons has been suggested (Higgins and Barrnett, 1971). After absorption of products of interluminal digestion and synthesis of the CoA derivatives of the absorbed fatty acids, triglycerides are resynthesized by a pathway involving acylation of monoglyceride, the enzymes of which are associated with the smooth endoplasmic reticulum at the apex of the cell immediately below the terminal web. Triglyceride droplets thus accumulate within these membranous envelopes. The membrane-bound droplets then move to the Golgi region, where they apparently fuse with the elements of the concave surface.

Phospholipids, the second major component of chylomicrons, are synthesized by a pathway involving acylation of α-glycerophosphate, the enzymes of which are associated with the rough endoplasmic reticulum. The phospholipid may move directly from its site of synthesis to triglyceride droplets in contiguous smooth-surfaced regions of the endoplasmic reticulum. Alternatively, it may move separately within pinched-off smooth vesicles to the outer elements of the Golgi region. At some point during this process, the triglyceride and phospholipid are packaged with cholesterol, cholesterol esters, and a small amount of protein to yield chylomicrons, which have a fairly constant composition and structure. These move to the lateral surfaces of the cell within membranous envelopes apparently derived from the Golgi region, and are released at this site.

Studies of Membrane Biogenesis

Cellular membranes have two major components: lipid, and protein (Korn, 1968). In most membranes, the lipid consists mainly of glycerophospholipid, which is synthesized by acylation of α-glycerophosphate by the pathway indicated earlier. It is reasonably well established that synthesis of the protein component of membranes occurs in association with ribosomes either free or bound. Knowledge of the site of synthesis of the phospholipid component would therefore be of value in gaining an understanding of the mechanism of membrane biogenesis. Cytochemical studies of the acyltransferases involved in the synthesis of phospholipids in tissue in which membrane biogenesis is taking place have therefore contributed significantly to this area of cell biology.

Biogenesis of plasma membranes in salt glands of salt-stressed ducklings. In response to salt water stress, the salt glands of domestic ducklings undergo hypertrophy. At a fine structural level, this is characterized by a marked increase in the plasma membrane, which is probably involved in the secretory function of the salt gland (Ellis *et al.,* 1963; Ernst and Ellis, 1969). By using the manganous-ferrocyanide method, it has been demonstrated that in the stressed salt gland the acyltransferases involved in synthesis of phospholipid are associated with the Golgi lamellae. In addition, vesicles morphologically resembling the plasma membrane have been observed between the Golgi region and the cell surface (Levine *et al.,* 1972). These observations were interpreted as indicating that the phospholipid component of the plasma membrane is synthesized in the Golgi region; the protein component may be synthesized either by free ribosomes, which occur in large numbers in the secretory cells, or by bound ribosomes. The Golgi region may thus be the site of packaging of the plasma membrane components, from which site vesicles of membrane move to fuse with preexisting plasma membrane.

Biogenesis of smooth endoplasmic reticular membranes in the hepatocytes of phenobarbital-treated rats. In response to intraperitoneal injections of phenobarbital, there is a marked increase in the smooth endoplasmic reticulum of rat hepatocytes (Remmer and Merkel, 1963; Orrhenius and Ericsson, 1966; Staübli *et al.,* 1969). Accompanying this morphological change is an increase in the specific activity of the enzymes involved in the detoxification of phenobarbital (Ernster and Orrhenius, 1965; Orrhenius, 1965), which appears to be synthesized in the rough endoplasmic reticulum prior to appearing in the smooth endoplasmic reticulum. It is thus fairly well established that the enzymes of the smooth membranes are synthesized by the ribosomes of the rough membranes.

The site of synthesis of the phospholipids is, however, less clear. By using the manganous-ferrocyanide method for the fine structural localization of acyltransferases, it has been demonstrated that in the normal rat liver these enzymes are associated with the rough endoplasmic reticulum and to a lesser extent with the smooth endoplasmic reticulum (Figs. 2–10, 2–11, 2–12). On treatment of the rats with phenobarbital, however, when the smooth membranes proliferate, the acyltransferases involved in synthesis of phospholipid are associated with the smooth membranes and considerably reduced in the rough membranes. In view of these observations, it has been postulated that the phospholipid of the smooth endoplasmic reticular membranes is synthesized *in situ* and that the protein component is synthesized in the rough endoplasmic reticulum and inserted into sites of newly synthesized phospholipid (Higgins and Barrnett, 1972).

Biogenesis of myelin in the trigeminal nerve of the developing rat. The trigeminal nerve of rat undergoes myelination from the period of parturition to fifteen days after birth. There is an extremely high increase in the myelin membrane content around the eighth day after parturition, during which time the acyltransferase activity of the whole nerve shows a rapid rise (Benes, *et al.,* 1973). By using the copper-ferrocyanide method for the localization of acyltransferases, it has been demonstrated that in the Schwann cell undergoing myelination, acyltransferase activity involved in phospholipid synthesis is associated with Golgi-like elements, with vesicles between the Golgi region and the cell surface and with the cell surface, but absent from the mature and partially formed myelin. These results suggest that the Golgi membranes are the site of phospholipid synthesis in myelin formation. However, in contrast to the salt gland, the acyltransferases also appear to be active after the membrane vesicles leave the Golgi region and in the Schwann cell plasma membrane itself. In this case, in which the final membrane has a high lipid-to-protein ratio compared with other plasma membranes, lipid synthesis may continue for some time in the plasma membrane.

CONCLUDING REMARKS

At the time of writing, the cytochemical methods for the acyltransferases are the only ones involved in the fine structural localization of enzymes involved in biosynthetic processes. These enzymes are extremely important in the synthesis of cellular membranes, and, as briefly indicated in the last section, an investigation of the organization of the cell in membrane biogenesis has been the major application of the available methods. However, these enzymes play other roles in cellular organization, and the methods indicated may be applied to the localization of any of this group of enzymes. It must be reemphasized, however, that acyltransferases are susceptible both to fixation and to heavy metals. Before attempting to develop new methods for the localization of any of this group of enzymes, it is essential to perform both biochemical and cytochemical control experiments as indicated.

Cytochemical methods provide unique information not attainable with any other technique. Thus, from the present chapter, it may be seen that it is possible to localize enzymic activity to one side of a membrane or to specific organelles. The use of cell fractionation, although it provides quantitative measurements, does not allow this subtlety of localization.

REFERENCES

Benes, F. M., Higgins, J. A., and Barrnett, R. J. (1973). Ultrastructural localization of phospholipid synthesis in the rat trigemminal nerve, *J. Cell Biol.* **57**, 613.

Benes, F. M., Higgins, J. A., and Barrnett, R. J. (1972). Fine structural localization of acyltransferase activity in rat hepatocyte, *J. Histochem,. Cytochem.* **20**, 1031.

Bremer, J. (1962). Carnitine in intermediary metabolism: Reversible acetylation of carnitine by mitochondria. *J. Biol. Chem.* **237**, 2228.

Bressler, R., and Brendel, K. (1966). The role of carnitine and carnitine acetyltransferase in biological acetylations and fatty acid synthesis. *J. Biol. Chem.* **241,** 4092.

Brindley, D. N., and Hubscher, G. (1965). The intracellular distribution of the enzymes catalyzing the biosynthesis of glycerides in the intestinal mucosa. *Biochim. Biophys. Acta* **104,** 495.

Cardell, R. R., Badenhauser, S., and Porter, K. R. (1967). Intestinal triglyceride absorption in the rat. *J. Cell Biol.* **34,** 123.

Clark, B., and Hubscher, G. (1961). Synthesis of glycerides in subcellular fractions of intestinal mucosa. *Biochim. Biophys. Acta* **46,** 479.

Dawson, A. M., and Isselbacher, K. J. (1960a). The esterification of palmitate ^{14}C by homogenates of intestinal mucosa. *J. Clin. Invest.* **39,** 150.

Dawson, A. M., and Isselbacher, K. J. (1960b). Studies of lipid metabolism in the small intestine with observations of the role of bile salts. *J. Clin. Invest.* **39,** 730.

Eibl, H., Hill, E. E., and Lands, W. E. M. (1969). The subcellular distribution of acyltransferases which catalyse the synthesis of phosphoglycerides. *Europ. J. Biochem.* **9,** 250.

Ellis, R. A., Goertemiller, C. C., DeLellis, R. A., and Kablotski, Y. H. (1963). The effect of a salt water regime on the development of the salt glands of the domestic duckling. *Devel. Biol.* **8,** 286.

Ernst, S. A., and Ellis, R. A. (1969). The development of surface specialization in the secretory epithelium of the avian salt gland in response to osmotic stress. *J. Cell Biol.* **40,** 305.

Ernster, L., and Orrhenius, S. (1965). Substrate induced synthesis of the hydrolsating system of the liver microsomes. *Fed. Proc.* **25,** 1195.

Fritz, I. B., and Schultz, S. K. (1965). Carnitine acetyltransferase II Inhibition by carnitine analogues and by sulphydryl reagents. *J. Biol. Chem.* **240,** 2188.

Fritz, I. B., and Yue, K. (1964). Effects of carnitine on acetyl CoA oxidation by heart muscle mitochondria. *Am. J. Physiol.* **206,** 531.

Hayat, M. A. (1970). *Principles and Techniques of Electron Microscopy: Biological Applications,* Vol. 1. Van Nostrand Reinhold Company, New York and London.

Hayat, M. A. (1972). *Basic Electron Microscopy Techniques.* Van Nostrand Reinhold Company, New York and London.

Hayat, M. A. (1973). Specimen preparation. In: *Electron Microscopy of Enzymes: Principles and Methods,* Vol. 1 (Hayat, M. A., ed). Van Nostrand Reinhold Company, New York and London.

Higgins, J. A., and Barrnett, R. J. (1970). Cytochemical localization of transferase activities carnitine acetyltransferase. *J. Cell Sci.* **6,** 29.

Higgins, J. A., and Barrnett, R. J. (1971). Fine structural localization of acetyltransferases the monoglyceride and α-glycerophosphate pathways in intestinal absorptive cells. *J. Cell Biol.* **50,** 102.

Higgins, J. A., and Barrnett, R. J. (1972). Studies on the biogenesis of smooth endoplasmic reticular membranes in hepatocytes of phenobarbital treated rats. I. The site of activity of the acyltransferases involved in synthesis of membrane phospholipid. *J. Cell Biol.* **55,** 282.

Holloway, P. W. (1970). Steroid metabolism in *Lipid Metabolism* (Wakil, S. J., ed.), p. 371. Academic Press, New York.

Hubscher, G. B., Clark, B., Webb, M. E., and Sherrat, H. S. A. (1963). Structure and enzymatic relationships in intestinal fat metabolism. *Biochim. Biophys. Acta* **1,** 201.

Johnston, J. M. (1959). The absorption of fat by the isolated intestine. *J. Biol. Chem.* **234**, 1065.

Johnston, J. M. (1968). Mechanism of fat absorption. In: *Handbook of Physiology,* Section 63, p. 1353.

Johnston, J. M., and Brown, J. L. (1962). Intestinal utilization of double labelled monopalmitin. *Biochim. Biophys. Acta* **59**, 500.

Johnston, J. M., Rao, G. A., and Lowe, P. A. (1967). The separation of the α-glycerophosphate and monoglyceride pathways in the intestinal biosynthesis of triglyceride. *Biochim. Biophys. Acta* **137**, 578.

Karnovsky, M. L., and Roots, L. (1964). A "direct colouring" thiocholine method for cholinesterases. *J. Histochem. Cytochem.* **12**, 219.

Kern, F., and Borgstrom, B. (1965). Quantitative study of the pathways of triglyceride synthesis by hamster intestinal mucosa. *Biochim. Biophys. Acta* **98**, 520.

Kidby, D. K. (1969). Direct spectrophotometric estimation of ferrocyanide and its possible uses in sulphydryl oxidation studies. *Anal. Biochem.* **28**, 230.

Korn, E. D. (1968). The structure and function of the plasma membrane. *J. Gen. Physiol.* **52**, 257.

Lands, W. E. M., and Hart, P. (1965). Metabolism of glycerolipids. VI. specificity of acyl CoA: phospholipid acyltransferases. *J. Biol. Chem.* **240**, 1905.

Levine, A. M., Higgins, J. A., and Barrnett, R. J. (1972). Biogenesis of plasma membranes in salt glands of salt stressed ducklings: Localization of acyltransferase activity. *J. Cell Sci.* **11**, 855.

Marquis, N. R., and Fritz, I. B. (1965). The distribution of carnitine, acetylcarnitine, and carnitine acetyltransferase in rat tissue. *J. Biol. Chem.* **240**, 2193.

Mizutani, A., and Barrnett, R. J. (1965). Fine structural demonstration of phosphatase activity at pH 9.0. *Nature* **206**, 1001.

Norum, K. R., Farstad, N., and Bremer, B. (1966). The submitochondrial distribution of acid CoA ligase and palmityl CoA: Carnitine palmityl transferase in rat liver mitochondria. *Biochem. Biophys. Res. Commun.* **24**, 797.

Orrhenius, S. (1965). Further studies on the induction of the drug hydroxylating enzyme system of liver microsomes. *J. Cell Biol.* **26**, 725.

Orrhenius, S., and Ericsson, J. L. E. (1966). Enzyme-membrane relationships in phenobarbital induction of synthesis of drug metabolising enzyme system and proliferation of endoplasmic membranes. *J. Cell Biol.* **28**, 181.

Overton, J. (1967). Localized lanthanum staining of the intestinal brush border. *J. Cell Biol.* **35**, 100A.

Rao, G. A., and Johnston, J. M. (1966). Purification and properties of triglyceride synthesis from the intestinal mucosa. *Biochim. Biophys. Acta* **125**, 465.

Remmer, H., and Merkel, H. J. (1963). Drug induced changes in liver endoplasma reticulum associated with drug metabolising enzymes. *Science* **142**, 1657.

Senior, J. R. (1964). Intestinal absorption of fat. *J. Lipid Res.* **5**, 495.

Staübli, W., Hess, R., and Weibel, E. R. (1969). Correlated morphometric and biochemical studies on the liver cell. II. Effects of phenobarbital on rat hepatocytes. *J. Cell Biol.* **42**, 92.

Wakil, S. J. (1970). Fatty Acid Metabolism in *Lipid Metabolism* (Wakil, S. J., ed.), p. 1. Academic Press, New York.

3
Polyphenoloxidases (Plants)

YVETTE CZANINSKI AND ANNE-MARIE CATESSON

Laboratoire de Botanique, Ecole Normale Supérieure and Institut de Biologie Végétale, Université Paris VI, Paris, France

INTRODUCTION

Phenols comprise one of the most important groups of plant compounds. They are involved in a number of reactions, including wall thickening, electron transport, and resistance to infections. Polyphenoloxidases (PPO) take part in these reactions, and it is known that the majority of the plant cells show significant *o*-diphenoloxidase activities. At present, the localization of the activity of these enzymes at the subcellular level is incompletely known, and a need has been felt to design better histochemical and cytochemical methods. Several authors (Czaninski and Catesson, 1972; Parish, 1972a) have recently attempted to develop techniques for the ultrastructural localization of PPO in plant tissues; these techniques are based on the methodology that has been developed for the localization of tyrosinases in animal tissues (Novikoff *et al.,* 1968; Okun *et al.,* 1970; see also Eppig, in this volume).

The term polyphenoloxidase has been used for a long time (see Bonner, 1957), although the terms phenolase, phenoloxidase, catecholoxidase, and tyrosinase have been used as synonyms. The classification of these enzymes is difficult, for some of them act both as polyphenoloxidases and as hydroxylases. These enzymes can be divided into two main groups—ortho-diphenoloxidases (EC.1.10.3.1), and para-diphenoloxidases (EC.1.10.3.2) and have been subdivided into two classes (Robb *et al.,* 1965).

Tyrosinases

These enzymes can, like tyrosinase, catalyze both ortho-hydroxylation of monophenols and the oxidation of ortho-diphenols. The former activity is called cresolase, and the latter catecholase. A tyrosine hydroxylase (EC. 1.14.3) has, however, been isolated as well (Udenfriend, 1966; Molinoff and Axelrod, 1971). Such enzymes are present in both animal and plant tissues; for further details, the reader is referred to Eppig, in this volume.

Ortho-diphenoloxidases

These enzymes, unlike tyrosinases, are devoid of hydroxylation properties and act only on *o*-diphenols. They have been found in plants such as tea (Gregory and Bendall, 1966), tobacco (Clayton, 1959), and sweet potato (Eiger and Dawson, 1949). However, in most of the published studies involving the use of *o*-diphenols as a substrate, the enzymes have not been specified as belonging to the first or the second group.

Many years ago, several workers had already postulated simultaneously the existence of different *o*-diphenoloxidases in plants such as tobacco and mushroom (Sisler and Evans, 1958; Clayton, 1959). Subsequently, numerous workers have shown the presence of PPO isozymes in various plants. For example, three have been found in tea (Takeo and Baker, 1973), four in peach (Wong *et al.,* 1971), six in tobacco (Van Loon, 1971), up to eleven in potato, and twelve in *Agaricus* (Constantinides and Bedford, 1967). These enzymes have characteristic optimum pH, response to inhibitors, affinity for certain substrates, and presence in certain types of cells. The activity of DOPAoxidase and 4-methyl-catecholoxidase, for instance, has been found to be limited to the chlorophyll-containing membranes in beet leaves; and hydroxylase activity seemed also to be abundant in the chloroplast fraction; the enzymatic affinity was found to be stronger for DOPA than for 4-methylcatechol in the mitochondrial fraction (Parish, 1972a and b).

Para-diphenoloxidases (EC.1.10.3.2)

These enzymes act on para-diphenols such as hydroquinone and *p*-phenylenediamines. Laccases can be classified in this category of enzymes. They are also usually capable of oxidizing *o*-diphenols (e.g., catechol). These enzymes, however, differ from other PPO enzymes because of their almost complete insensitivity to inhibition by carbon monoxide (Bonner, 1957). Not all laccases possess the same affinity for substrates. For example, laccases present in the poppy, in contrast to fungal laccases, do not oxidize phenols having ortho-methoxy groups (e.g., guaiacol) (Roberts, 1971).

METHODS

Principle of the Reaction

Methodology for the localization of PPO activity at the light microscope level was developed early (Lison, 1960; Barka and Anderson, 1963). The quinones, liberated by the oxidation of polyphenols, are highly reactive. With catechol as a substrate, the quinone formed combines with the ambient proteins yielding a reddish brown color (Arvy, 1957). Novikoff et al. (1968) applied the DOPA reaction, as used in light microscopy (Becker et al., 1935), to electron microscopy, in order to demonstrate the activity of tyrosinase. The reaction of tyrosinase with tyrosine or DOPA results in the formation of a black reaction product. Subsequently, attempts were made to adapt this method for plant tissues (Czaninski and Catesson, 1972; Parish, 1972a).

The principle of this reaction involves obtaining an insoluble, electron-dense reaction product from a synthetic substrate, as is the case when DAB is used as a substrate for peroxidase activity (osmiophilic staining principle) (see Shnitka and Seligman, 1971). Ortho-diphenols possess the property of reacting with metals through chelation (Ribereau-Gayon, 1968). Some ortho-diphenols, if not all, are also capable of forming compounds with osmium tetroxide. This property explains the electron density of complex polyphenolic compounds such as anthocyanins and tannins. O-diquinones, resulting from the oxidation of o-diphenols, are even more reactive than are the latter, and readily form addition products with osmium tetroxide (see Eppig, in this volume). Furthermore, o-diquinone molecules can cross-link among themselves or/and with surrounding proteins (Mason and Peterson, 1965; Pierpoint, 1969). This probably results in the formation of a stable osmiophilic complex which imparts electron density to the reaction product.

Choice of the Substrate

In general, the properties mentioned above are common to all o-diquinones. A wide choice of substrates is therefore available among o-diphenols, which should facilitate specific ultrastructural localization of various o-diphenoloxidases. However, only DOPA has been employed in the published studies.

We have experimented with 4-methylcatechol as a substrate, and the oxidation product is electron-dense. However, the results obtained are less satisfactory than those yielded by DOPA. This point will be discussed later.

No information is available on the possible interaction between p-diquinones and osmium tetroxide. Since metal compounds can be obtained only with o-diphenols, and since p-diquinones show little reactivity, the addition of osmium tetroxide must occur less readily to the latter than to the former.

Experimental Conditions

Polyphenoloxidases show little inhibition by aldehydes, which makes it possible to use conventional fixatives such as glutaraldehyde prior to incubation for relatively long durations. This advantage is especially significant in the case of plant tissues which are difficult to fix.

In order to be certain regarding the nature of the enzyme and the specificity of the reaction, the use of control preparations is necessary. In addition to the normal controls (absence of the substrate or heat inhibition) for the study of any enzymatic reaction, sodium diethyldithiocarbamate (DDC) can be employed as an inhibitor. It was thought for a long time that DDC was a specific inhibitor for copper-containing enzymes, particularly for PPO. However, recent studies have shown that this substance also acts on peroxidases (Okun *et al.*, 1970). Oxidation of catechol, on the other hand, is sensitive to the action of cyanide (Lison, 1960), which also affects other oxidases.

When studying PPO, it is important to be aware of secondary reactions, particularly with regard to oxidation of substrates by peroxidases. In order to differentiate peroxidases from PPO in the absence of a specific inhibitor, a control inhibition with catalase (0.1 mg/ml) is desirable. Catalase prevents any peroxidase activity by destroying hydrogen peroxide, which might be present (Okun *et al.*, 1970; see Van Loon, 1971). Some samples should be incubated in DAB for possible demonstration of peroxidase.

Fixation

Fixation of thin slices of plant tissues is carried out in the cold (0–4°C) for 90 min in the following solution:

25% glutaraldehyde	1 ml
Distilled water	1 ml
0.075 M sodium cacodylate buffer (pH 7.4)	4 ml

Sucrose or glucose is added to the buffer to obtain a molarity close to that of the tissue under study. In the case of tobacco leaves and potato tubers, the buffer molarity is raised to 0.4 to 0.6 M. Similarly, the molarity of all the baths and alcohols is raised. The tissue specimens are thoroughly washed in the buffer (at least 3 baths of 1 hr each).

After incubation, the specimens are thoroughly washed with distilled water containing sucrose, postfixed with 1% osmium tetroxide in the buffer (pH 7.4) having a suitable molarity, and embedded according to standard procedures (Hayat, 1970 and 1973). Ultrathin sections are examined without additional staining.

Incubation in the Presence of DOPA

The incubation is carried out in the following freshly prepared medium (Novikoff *et al.,* 1968; Okun *et al.,* 1970):

> Sörensen's phosphate buffer (0.067 M, pH 7.0)   10 ml
> DOPA (d,1,3,4-dihydroxiphenylalanine)   50 mg

The best results for tobacco leaves and potato tubers are obtained with a preincubation of 18 hr at 0.4°C followed by 1 hr incubation at 37°C.

The controls are prepared by pretreating the tissue with DDC (0.02 M), washing thoroughly, and then incubating in DOPA. Under these conditions, tyrosinase or PPO can be differentiated from peroxidase. Other specimens are subjected, prior to incubation, to 100°C temperature for 10 min.

Results in tobacco leaves. In the young leaves (1 to 2 cm long), electron-dense reaction products were seen in thylakoids, completely filling the saccules (Figs. 3–1, 3–3, 3–6). Only the granary and intergranary thylakoids showed the reaction product; the double membrane of the plastid did not show any deposits. The stroma did not appear to be more electron-dense than in the controls. Other organelles (mitochondria, dictyosomes, endoplasmic reticulum, and plasmalemma) did not show any positive reaction. The fact that plastids of all control preparations, particularly those subjected to heat, showed lamellae free from any reaction deposits

----

All specimens were fixed with glutaraldehyde followed by osmium tetroxide; sections were examined without poststaining. *cw,* cell wall; *er,* endoplasmic reticulum; *I,* inclusion; *is,* intracellular space; *m,* mitochondrion; *N,* nucleus; *p,* plastid; *pe,* peroxysome; *s,* starch; *t,* thylakoid; *v,* vacuole; *ve,* vesicle.

Figs. 3–1 and 3–2. Tobacco leaves incubated in DOPA. Both chloroplasts and amyloplasts show the reaction product. However, some amyloplasts show little deposition. Other organelles are devoid of any reaction product. Fig. 3–1, X5,500; Fig. 3–2, X9,500.

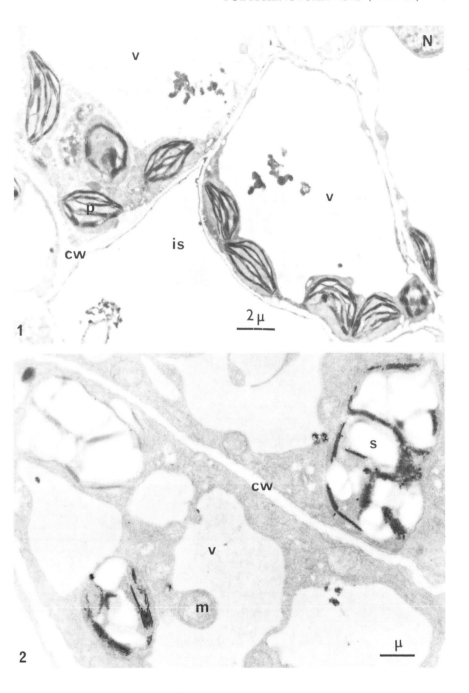

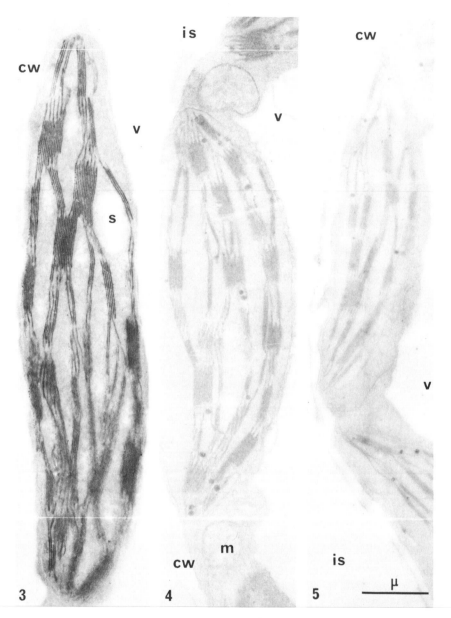

Figs. 3–3, 3–4, 3–5. Tobacco leaves incubated only in DOPA (Fig. 3–3), in DOPA after heating for 10 min (Fig. 3–4), or without DOPA (Fig. 3–5). Only Fig. 3–3 shows the reaction product; no electron-dense deposits are found after heating or incubation in a medium without DOPA. ×20,000.

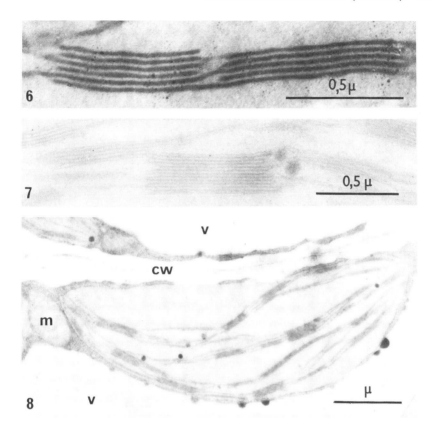

Figs. 3–6, 3–7, 3–8. Tobacco leaves. Fig. 3–6 shows details of a plastid incubated in DOPA. Note the presence of electron-dense deposits within the thylakoid. X69,000. Fig. 3–7 shows details of a plastid incubated without DOPA. No electron-dense deposits are visible within the thylakoid. X57,000. Fig. 3–8 shows a plastid incubated in DOPA and DDC. No reaction product is visible within the plastid. X20,000.

points to the occurrence of DOPA enzymatic oxidation (Figs. 3–4, 3–5, 3–7, 3–8). The results were identical in plastids of all categories of observed foliar cells such as stomata, chlorenchyma, procambium, and vascular cambium. Amylyferous (Fig. 3–2) or nonamylyferous (Figs. 3–1 and 3–3) plastids showed similar results.

In adult leaves, containing a substantial amount of chlorophyll, some plastids showed the same strong positive reaction as that shown by young leaves. However, in the same cell, a large number of plastids were free of oxidative DOPA activities.

Results in potato tubers. Both fresh potatoes and small slices after 24 hr of aging in water were studied. These specimens have abundant amylo-

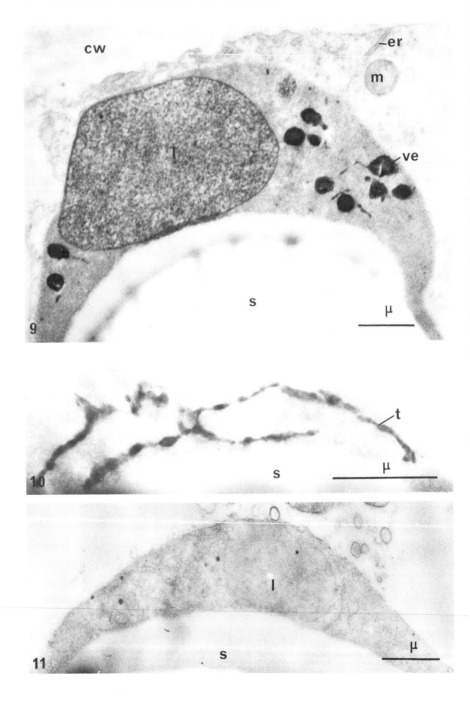

plasts and little stroma. The lamellae in the plastids were more numerous in the aged specimens. The thylakoids and vesicles were, in general, rich in the reaction products (Figs. 3–9, 3–10). The stroma sometimes contained a granular inclusion which showed a heavy deposition when the specimens were incubated in the presence of DOPA (Fig. 3–9). No other cellular structure showed positive reaction. Control preparations did not show any reaction product either in the plastids or in any other organelle (Fig. 3–11).

Incubation in the Presence of 4-Methylcatechol

As mentioned previously, we tested a second substrate. The specimens are incubated in 0.1 M 4-methylcatechol prepared in 0.1 M phosphate buffer (pH 6.5) containing sucrose. The medium should be prepared immediately prior to use (Siegenthaler, personal communication). The procedure is identical to that described previously for DOPA. We tried an additional inhibition by incubating the specimens in the whole medium to which had been added 0.01 M KCN.

Results. In young sycamore leaves and adult carnation leaves (Czaninski and Catesson, in preparation), the reaction product is apparent in the peroxysomes of the majority of the foliar cells. In addition, the internal membrane and cristae of mitochondria showed the reaction product (Fig. 3–12). On the other hand, thylakoids showed little reaction product. Therefore, the oxidation products of 4-methylcatechol can provide, in the presence of osmium tetroxide, a product which is electron-dense. The specificity of the reaction is discussed below.

CONCLUDING REMARKS

The available evidence indicates that DOPA yields satisfactory ultrastructural localization of DOPA-oxidase activity, at least in the plastids of tobacco and potato. The observed reaction is of a distinct enzymatic nature, since it is inhibited by a 10 min heating at 100°C. It is not possible that this oxidation is due to endogenous peroxidase, because peroxidase activ-

---

Figs. 3–9, 3–10, 3–11. Slices of a potato tuber aged in water for 24 hr. Figs. 3–9 and 3–10 show reaction deposits within the vesicles and thylakoids after incubation in DOPA. The inclusion also shows positive reaction. Fig. 3–9, ×17,000; Fig. 3–10, ×32,000. Fig. 3–11 shows absence of any reaction product after incubation in DOPA and DDC. ×17,000.

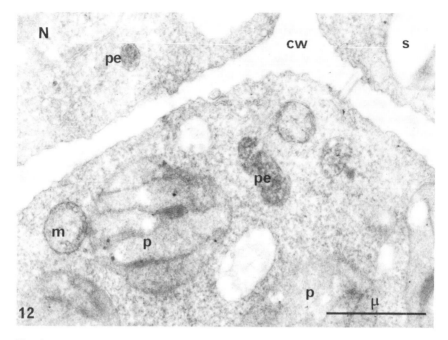

Fig. 3–12. A sycamore leaf incubated in 4-methylcatechol. No reaction product is visible within the plastids, but it is present within peroxisomes. Mitochondrial cristae and inner membrane show a slight positive reaction. ×30,000.

ity has not been detected in plastids. However, the presence of some other oxidizing enzymes, which may oxidize DOPA, cannot be ruled out.

On the other hand, positive reaction observed in peroxysomes by using 4-methylcatechol is probably due to a peroxysomal oxidase; polyphenol-oxidases have not been found in these organelles. Similarly, the role of mitochondrial oxidases in the deposition of osmium blacks on the internal membrane and cristae cannot be excluded. However, Parish (1972b) has shown that in beet leaves, a low catechol oxidative activity was associated with the mitochondrial fraction. As far as 4-methylcatechol is concerned, other verifications are necessary to remove the uncertainty.

With both substrates, the accuracy of the ultrastructural localization seems to be satisfactory, since little diffusion deposits or artifacts were observed. Furthermore, cytochemical observations are generally in agreement with the results obtained using biochemical methods (Mayer and Friend, 1960; Nye and Hampton, 1966; Siegenthaler and Vaucher-Bonjour, 1971).

The unsatisfactory results obtained with beets by Parish (1972a) were perhaps due to inadequate experimental conditions. Parish did not carry out any preincubation at 0 to 4°C in order to facilitate substrate penetration. However, we did not obtain better results after a preincubation in the DOPA medium in the case of carnation and sycamore specimens. The variations observed in the results discussed above suggest that optimal experimental parameters (adequate substrate or substrates, pH, temperature, and the duration of incubation) for each type of specimen must be determined.

It must be pointed out that the methods, except DOPA oxidase, used to localize PPO are at present less than satisfactory and need refinement. These methods are expected to play a key role in better understanding the complex relationships existing between PPO, polyphenols, and growth-promoting substances during the life of a plant. Also, it is hoped that these methods, as they develop, will be useful for cytochemistry of animal tissues.

We are indebted to Dr. A. Ben Abdenlkader for preparing the aged potato slices.

REFERENCES

Arvy, L. (1957–58). Les techniques actuelles d'histoenzymologie. *Biologie médicale,* **46.**

Barka, T., and Anderson, P. J. (1963). *Histochemistry.* Harper and Row, New York.

Becker, S. W., Praver, L. L., and Thatcher, H. (1935). Improved (paraffin section) method for dopa reaction with considerations of dopa positive cells, as studied by this method. *Arch. Derm. Syph.* (Chicago), **31,** 190.

Bonner, W. D., Jr., 1957. Soluble oxidases and their functions. *Ann. Rev. Plant Physiol.* **8,** 427.

Clayton, R. A. (1959). Properties of tobacco polyphenoloxidase. *Arch. Biochem. Biophys.* **81,** 404.

Constantinides, S. M., and Bedford, C. L. (1967). Multiple forms of phenoloxidase. *J. Food Sc.* **32,** 446.

Czaninski, Y., and Catesson, A. M. (1972). Localisation ultrastructurale d'activités polyphénoloxydasiques dans les chloroplastes de *Nicotiana glutinosa. J. Microscopie* **15,** 409.

Eiger, I. Z., and Dawson, C. R. (1949). Sweet potato phenolase. Preparation, properties, and determination of protein content. *Arch. Biochem.* **21,** 194.

Gregory, R. P. F., and Bendall, D. S. (1966). The purification and some properties of the polyphenol oxidase from tea (*Camellia sinensis* L.). *Biochem. J.* **101,** 569.

Hayat, M. A. (1970). *Principles and Techniques of Electron Microscopy: Biological Applications,* Vol. 1. Van Nostrand Reinhold Company, New York and London.

Hayat, M. A. (1972). *Basic Electron Microscope Techniques.* Van Nostrand Reinhold Company, New York and London.

Hayat, M. A. (1973). Specimen preparation. In: *Electron Microscopy of Enzymes: Principles and Methods,* Vol. 1 (Hayat, M. A., ed.). Van Nostrand Reinhold Company, New York and London.

Lison, L. (1960). *Histochimie et cytochimie animales.* Gauthier-Villars, ed. Paris.

Mason, H. S., and Peterson, E. W. (1965). Melanoproteins. I. Reactions between enzyme generated quinones and amino acids. *Biochim. Biophys. Acta* **111,** 134.

Mayer, A. M., and Friend, J. (1960). Properties and solubility of phenolase in isolated chloroplasts. *Nature* **185,** 464.

Molinoff, P. B., and Axelrod, J. (1971). Biochemistry of catecholamines. *Ann. Rev. Biochem.* **40,** 465.

Novikoff, A. B., Albala, A., and Biempica, L. (1968). Ultrastructural and cytochemical observations on B-16 and Harding-Passey mouse melanomas. The origin of premelanosomes and compound melanosomes. *J. Histochem. Cytochem.* **16,** 299.

Nye, T. G., and Hampton, R. E. (1966). Biochemical of tobacco ETCH virus infection on tobacco leaf tissue. II. Polyphenoloxidase activity in subcellular fractions. *Phytochemistry* **5,** 1187.

Okun, M. R., Edelstein, L. M., Or, N., Hamada, G., Donnellan, B., and Lever, W. F., 1970. Histochemical differentiation of peroxidase mediated from tyrosinase-mediated melanin formation in mammalian tissues. *Histochemie* **23,** 295.

Parish, R. W. (1972a). The intracellular location of phenol oxidases and peroxidase in stems of spinach beet (*Beta vulgaris* L.). *Zeit. f. Pflanzenphysiologie* **66,** 176.

Parish, R. W. (1972b). The intracellular location of phenol oxidases peroxidase and phosphatases in the leaves of spinach beet (*Beta vulgaris* L. subspecies *vulgaris*). *Eur. J. Biochem.* **31,** 446.

Pierpoint, W. S. (1969). *O*-quinones formed in plant extracts: Their reaction with bovine serum albumin. *Biochem. J.* **112,** 619.

Ribereau, Gayon P. (1968). *Les composés phénoliques des végétaux.* Dunod, ed. Paris (English edition, 1972).

Robb, D. A., Mapson, L. W., and Swain, T. (1965). On the heterogeneity of the tyrosinase of broad bean (*Vicia faba* L.). *Phytochem.* **4,** 731.

Roberts, M. F. (1971). Polyphenolases in the 1000 g fraction of *Papaver somniferum* latex. *Phytochem.* **10,** 3021.

Shnitka, T. K., and Seligman, A. M. (1971). Ultrastructural localization of enzymes. *Ann. Rev. Biochem.* **40,** 375.

Siegenthaler, P., and Vaucher-Bonjour, P. (1971). Vieillissement de l'appareil photosynthétique. III. Variations et caractéristiques de l'activité *o*-diphénoloxydase (polyphénoloxydase) au cours du vieillissement in vitro de chloroplastes isolés d'épinard. *Planta* **100,** 106.

Sisler, E. C., and Evans, H. J. (1958). A comparison of chlorogenic acid and catechol as substrates for the polyphenoloxidase from tobacco and mushroom. *Plant Physiol.* **33,** 255.

Takeo, T., and Baker, J. E. (1973). Changes in multiple forms of polyphenol oxidase during maturation of tea leaves. *Phytochem.* **12,** 21.

Udenfriend, S. (1966). Tyrosine hydroxylase. *Pharmacol. Rev.* **18,** 43.

Van Loon, L. C. (1971). Tobacco polyphenoloxidases: A specific staining method indicating non-identity with peroxidases. *Phytochem.* **10,** 503.

Wong, T. C., Luh, B. S., and Whitaker, J. R. (1971). Effect of phloroglucinol and resorcinol on the clingstone peach polyphenol oxidase-catalyzed oxidation of 4-methylcatechol. *Plant Physiol.* **48,** 24.

4

Tyrosinase

JOHN J. EPPIG, JR.

Biology Department, Brooklyn College
of CUNY, Brooklyn, New York

INTRODUCTION

Some cells are capable of converting tyrosine into a brown or black pigment called melanin. It has been known since the studies of Lerner *et al.* (1949) that in most cases the first two steps in this conversion—tyrosine to dihydroxyphenylalanine (DOPA), and DOPA to DOPA quinone—are catalyzed by a single enzyme called tyrosinase (Fig. 4–1). However, it is known that peroxidase also can convert tyrosine to DOPA, and DOPA to melanin *in vitro* (Okun *et al.*, 1972). Therefore it has been suggested that in some systems, peroxidase initially converts tyrosine to DOPA, and then tyrosinase oxidizes this DOPA to DOPA quinone (Okun *et al.*, 1972). This implication of peroxidase in melanin formation complicates the generally accepted notion that tyrosinase catalyzes both reactions. Nevertheless, tyrosinase appears to be required in at least the DOPA-to-DOPA-quinone reaction in most normal melanogenic systems.

Melanin-producing cells have for some time been identified by the technique, first described by Bloch (1917), of incubating pieces of tissue or sections in a solution of DOPA. Since the procedure involves the oxidation of DOPA, it is often referred to as the "DOPA reaction." After many

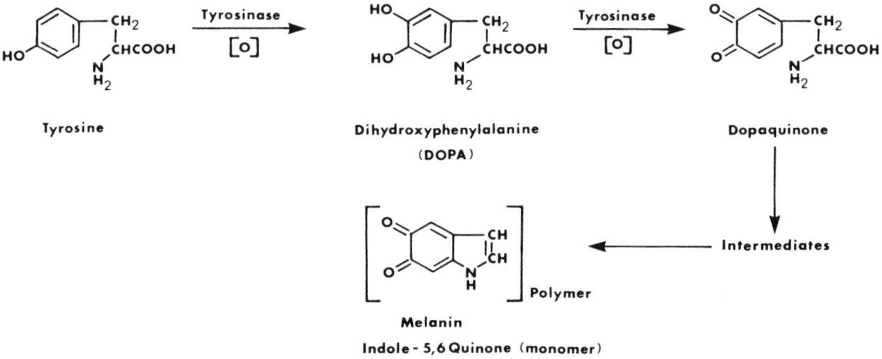

Fig. 4–1. Synthetic pathway for the synthesis of melanin.

years of debate (see Fitzpatrick *et al.*, 1967), it is now generally agreed that the darkening of the cytoplasm by the DOPA reaction is due, at least in part, to the action of tyrosinase.

Techniques for the ultrastructural localization of enzymes must provide the elements which will result in the production of an identifiable electron-opaque substance at the site of enzyme activity. In most cases, this is accomplished by the formation of electron-opaque precipitates of the enzyme reaction products. However, the electron-opaque material which results from the DOPA reaction and which indicates tyrosinase localization is the natural product itself (melanin or an immediate precursor).

Although the general theory and execution of the DOPA reaction is simple, it has been fraught with controversy since becoming a common histological procedure. The two main points of contention involve specificity and autooxidation of DOPA.

SPECIFICITY

Certain oxidative enzymes other than tyrosinase can convert tyrosine or DOPA to melanin. For example, cytochrome system enzymes are capable of oxidizing DOPA, but this problem is minimized because of inhibition by aldehyde fixation (Barka and Anderson, 1963). A problem causing greater concern has been presented by Okun *et al.* (1970 and 1972), who have shown that endogenous peroxidase can mediate the initial phases of melanin formation in histochemical and cytochemical preparations. These studies suggest that in certain systems, peroxidase may initially convert tyrosine to DOPA, and then tyrosinase oxidizes that DOPA to form DOPA quinone in the continuation of the melanin synthetic pathway.

However, since peroxidase can convert DOPA to melanin *in vitro* as well as tyrosine to DOPA, it becomes necessary to perform additional experiments on glutaraldehyde-fixed specimens to specify the enzyme (tyrosinase or peroxidase) giving a positive DOPA reaction.

Thus, samples should be subjected to incubation in the diaminobenzidine (DAB) medium of Graham and Karnovsky (1966) for the demonstration of endogenous peroxidase. A specimen of a known peroxidase-positive tissue such as liver should also be incubated in this medium to verify a successful peroxidase reaction. Another specimen should be preincubated in catalase (to eliminate H_2O_2 required by peroxidase) and then incubated in DOPA reaction medium containing catalase. This catalase treatment has been shown to eliminate peroxidase-dependent DOPA oxidation (Okun *et al.*, 1970 and 1972). The preincubation of samples in diethyldithiocarbonate (DDC) (10^{-2} M) eliminated DOPA oxidation, which is not mediated by peroxidase (Okun *et al.*, 1972). Hence, a positive DOPA reaction can be attributed to tyrosinase activity in a given location if the DAB reaction is negative; or when the DAB reaction is positive, the DOPA reaction is not affected after incubation with catalase, and/or the DOPA reaction is inhibited after preincubation with DDC.

AUTOOXIDATION

At an alkaline pH, DOPA is oxidized without the mediation of a catalyst. For this reason, DOPA solutions above pH 7.0 can darken within only a few hours. Therefore two techniques are commonly employed to reduce the nonspecific background staining which results from the autooxidation of DOPA: (1) adjusting the pH to 6.8 to 6.9 in the phosphate-buffered DOPA solution, and (2) preparing the DOPA solution in cacodylate buffer at pH 7.42. A possible disadvantage to the first technique is that tissues must be incubated at a pH which is lower than that (pH 7.4) considered optimal for ultrastructural preservation during fixation. On the other hand, Rodriguez and McGavran (1969) have compared the effects of phosphate and other buffers on the DOPA reaction. They have found that the complete autooxidation of DOPA is inhibited and that the enzymatic oxidation of DOPA is favored by cacodylate buffer. Therefore this writer prefers the DOPA solution in cacodylate buffer even when the tissue has been fixed in a phosphate-buffered glutaraldehyde solution.

In order to further minimize the effects of DOPA autooxidation, tissues should be incubated for as little time as possible. Usually 1 to 2 hr incubation is sufficient, but when longer incubations are required, as shown by empirical experimentation, fresh DOPA medium should be substituted at least every 2 hr.

PROCEDURE

(1) Small (1 to 2 mm) pieces of tissue are fixed in 2 to 3% glutaraldehyde in phosphate buffer (pH 7.4) at 4°C for 1 to 2 hr. The tonicity of the fixation solution should be adjusted to provide optimal conditions for the specific tissue to be studied (see Hayat, 1970 and 1973). A Smith-Farquhar tissue chopper may be used to cut 40 μ sections if necessary after fixation. Monolayers of cells in culture may require only 15 min fixation. Some studies have shown that glutaraldehyde inhibits tyrosinase activity in certain subcellular fractions but not in others. It may be advisable, therefore, to incubate some unfixed pieces of tissue in the DOPA medium followed by glutaraldehyde fixation (Toda and Fitzpatrick, 1971).

(2) Wash the tissue for at least 15 min in 0.1 M phosphate or cacodylate buffer (pH 7.4) at 4°C. Insufficient washing may not remove all the glutaraldehyde, which could result in enzyme inhibition.

(3) Incubate the tissue in a 0.1% (w/v) solution of L-DOPA in 0.1 M cacodylate buffer at pH 7.4 for 1 to 2 hr. Mammalian tissues may be incubated at 37°C, but 25.5°C has been found to be optimal for amphibian tissues. If incubation must be longer than 2 hr, fresh DOPA medium should be substituted every 2 hr. For some tissues, it may be necessary to presoak the fixed tissue in L-DOPA solution in the cold for several hours, or even overnight, to ensure the penetration of substrate and the visualization of all enzyme sites, especially those with low levels of activity.

(4) After incubation, the tissue should be washed in two changes of 0.1 M phosphate buffer (pH 7.4) at 4°C for a total of 15 min.

(5) Postfix in 1% osmium tetroxide in 0.1 M phosphate buffer (pH 7.4) at 4°C for 2 hr.

(6) Proceed with standard Epon embedding, sectioning, and uranyl acetate-lead citrate staining procedures (see Hayat, 1972).

Additional Comments on the Procedure

Sucrose may be used to adjust the tonicity of any of the solutions. The L form of DOPA should be used instead of DL-DOPA since only the L form is utilized by the enzyme and since the D form would serve only to increase the hazards of autooxidation. The L-DOPA medium should always be freshly prepared. In addition to the specificity controls mentioned above, an additional control group should be incubated without the L-DOPA substrate. Optimal results are obtained if the entire procedure up to Epon infiltration is completed in a single day rather than storing the tissues after any step.

TYROSINASE ACTIVITY IN MELANIN GRANULES

It is difficult to differentiate between the natural tyrosinase reaction product and the DOPA reaction product, since they are both melanin. This is especially problematical when the investigator wishes to know whether the melanin granules in his particular system contain tyrosinase activity. Sometimes this question can be answered by a careful comparison of electron micrographs of control and DOPA-reacted melanin granules. For example, the periphery of late premelanosomes in frog embryo melanocytes have a scalloped appearance after the DOPA reaction which is not seen in the controls (Fig. 4–2). This is interpreted as an indication that tyrosinase activity is present at the periphery of the premelanosome (Eppig and Dumont, 1972). However, in many cases, the evidence of tyrosinase activity in melanin granules which is based on the DOPA reaction is uncertain. One way to resolve this problem is to isolate the melanin granules and to assay for tyrosinase activity by biochemical methods. Several methods have been described for the isolation of melanin granules (Baker et al., 1960; Seiji et al., 1963; Fierman and Demopoulos, 1971; Siakotos et al., 1973; Eppig and Dumont, 1974). Since each melanogenic system has its own characteristics, the investigator will have to adjust these procedures to meet the specific needs of his system and experiment.

After the melanin granules have been isolated, they may be assayed for tyrosinase activity. The procedures most suitable for the assay of such fractions are the radiometric assays of either Pomerantz (1966), Chen and Chavin (1965), or Achazi and Yamada (1972).

Representative melanin granule fractions should also be prepared for examination with the electron microscope to assay the purity of the preparations. Osmium tetroxide solution is added to the melanin granule suspension to a final concentration of one percent. After 15 to 30 min, the fixed granules are pelleted by centrifugation and the pellet prepared for sectioning and electron microscopy by the usual dehydration and embedding procedures.

CONCLUDING REMARKS

While analyzing the results of any enzyme localization in electron microscopic preparations, it should be kept in mind that even though reaction procedure is found in a particular subcellular component, the enzyme may not normally be *active* there in the living cell. For example, it may be that conformational changes in the enzyme structure during fixation may effectively separate the enzyme from an inhibitor molecule, or perhaps inhibi-

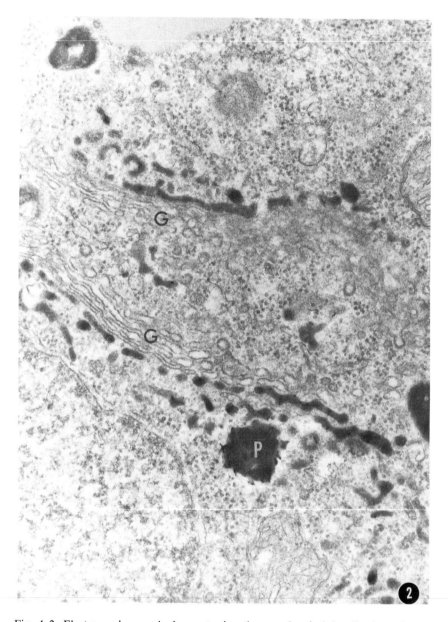

Fig. 4–2. Electron micrograph demonstrating the cytochemical localization of tyrosinase by the DOPA reaction in a skin melanocyte of a larval frog (*Xenopus laevis*). DOPA reaction product is seen in the distal cisterna of the Golgi complex (*G*) and in smooth surfaced tubules associated with the Golgi complex and a late premelanosome (*P*). Note the scalloped appearance of the premelanosome periphery indicating tyrosinase activity in this area. ×52,500.

tors are diluted out during the process of tissue preparation. These conditions might result in the visualization of the enzyme in a subcellular component where it is normally present but in an inactive state. It is therefore clear that the DOPA reaction and other enzyme localization procedures, unless they can be experimentally manipulated to show otherwise, demonstrate only where an enzyme is present and not necessarily where it is active in the living cell.

In addition to its use in localizing endogenous tyrosinase, the DOPA reaction has been utilized to monitor the uptake of exogenous tyrosinase which has been administered to trace the uptake of proteins by kidney tubule cells (Oliver and Essner, 1972). The same cytochemical procedures are used to demonstrate both endogenous and exogenous tyrosinase.

Endogenous tyrosinase has been localized by the DOPA reaction at the ultrastructural level by a number of investigators using a wide range of melanin-producing cells (Table 4–1).

In general, these studies have shown that tyrosinase is localized in the Golgi apparatus, smooth-surfaced vesicles or tubules associated with the Golgi complex, and developing premelanosomes (Figs. 4–2, 4–3, 4–4). These data therefore imply that the Golgi complex has some role in the development of melanosomes. Some of the more recent studies (Maul and Brumbaugh, 1971; Stanka, 1970; Ide, 1972; Eppig and Dumont, 1972) have indicated that premelanosomes originate in Golgi-associated smooth endoplasmic reticulum. Tyrosinase is subsequently transferred to them from the Golgi apparatus. The DOPA reaction has also been applied to studies on the effects of pigment mutations (Brumbaugh, 1971; Brumbaugh and Zieg, 1972) and UV irradiation (Hunter *et al.,* 1970) on the melanogenic mechanisms. Thus, the subcellular localization of tyrosinase by the DOPA reaction is a useful tool, especially when used in

Table 4–1

Melanogenic System	*Reference*
Human skin	Mishima (1964)
Squid ink gland	Vogel and McGregor (1964)
Mouse melanomas	Novikoff, *et al.* (1968)
UV-irradiated human melanocytes	Hunter *et al.* (1970)
Human malignant melanomas	Maul and Romsdahl (1970)
Retinal pigmented epithelium of chick embryos	Stanka (1970)
Regenerating fowl feather	Maul and Brumbaugh (1971)
Retinal and epidermal fowl melanocytes	Brumbaugh (1971)
Retinal and epidermal fowl melanocytes	Brumbaugh and Zieg (1972)
Retinal pigmented epithelium of amphibian larvae	Eppig and Dumont (1972)
Retinal pigmented epithelium of chick embryos	Ide (1972)
Developing oocytes of the frog, *Xenopus laevis*	Eppig and Dumont (1974)

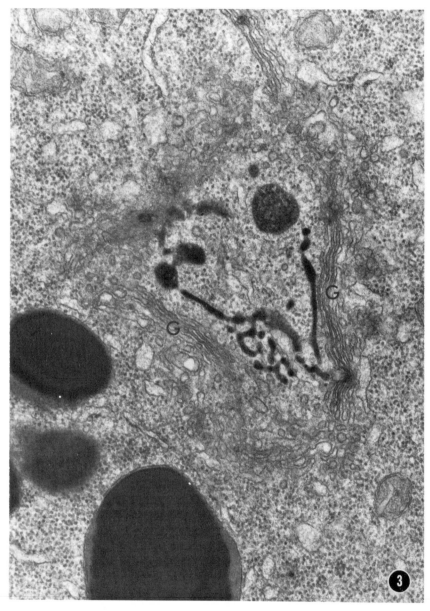

Fig. 4–3. Cytochemical localization of tyrosinase in a developing oocyte of the frog (*Xenopus laevis*). Reaction product is seen in the distal cisterna of the Golgi complex (*G*) and in an anastomosing network of smooth surfaced tubules associated with the distal cisterna of the Golgi apparatus. ×45,000.

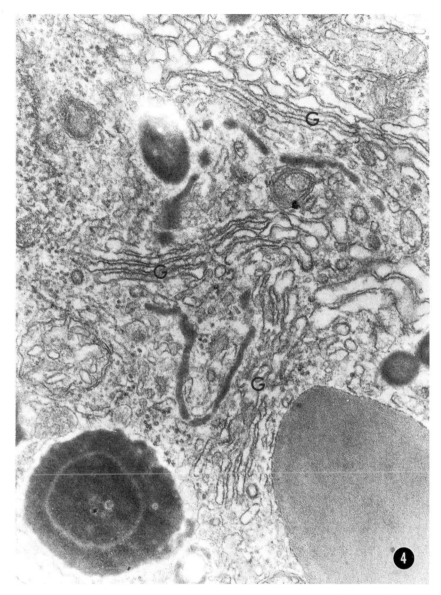

Fig. 4–4. An electron micrograph of a retinal pigmented epithelial cell of a larval frog (*Rana pipiens*). DOPA reaction product is seen in the distal cisterna of the Golgi complex (*G*). ×62,500.

connection with biochemical techniques, for the elucidation of the subcellular mechanisms of melanogenesis.

REFERENCES

Achazi, R., and Yamada, T. (1972). Tyrosinase activity in the Wolffian lens regenerating system. *Devel. Biol.* **27**, 295.

Baker, R. V., Birbeck, M. S. C., Blaschko, H., Fitzpatrick, T. B., and Seiji, M. (1960). Melanin granules and mitochondria. *Nature* **187**, 392.

Barka, T., and Anderson, P. (1963). *Histochemistry.* Hoeber Med. Div., Harper and Row, New York. Pp. 322, 329.

Bloch, B. (1917). Das Problem der Pigmentbildung in der Haut. *Arch. Dermat. u. Syph.* **124**, 129.

Brumbaugh, J. A. (1971). The ultrastructural effects of the *l* and *S* loci upon black-red melanin differentiation in the fowl. *Devel. Biol.* **24**, 392.

Brumbaugh, J. A., and Zieg, R. (1972). The ultrastructural effects of the dopa reaction upon developing retinal and epidermal melanocytes in the fowl. In: *Pigmentation: Its Genesis and Biologic Control* (Riley, V., ed.), p. 107. Appleton-Century-Crofts, New York.

Chen, Y. M., and Chavin, W. (1965). Radiometric assay of tyrosinase and theoretical considerations of melanin formation. *Anal. Biochem.* **13**, 234.

Eppig, J. J., Jr., and Dumont, J. N. (1972). Cytochemical localization of tyrosinase activity in pigmented epithelial cells of *Rana pipiens* and *Xenopus laevis* larvae. *J. Ultrastruct. Res.* **39**, 397.

Eppig, J. J., Jr., and Dumont, J. N. (1974). Oogenesis in *Xenopus laevis* (Daudin). III. The stimulation of tyrosinase activity and its subcellular localization. *Devel. Biol.* (*in press*).

Fierman, H., and Demopoulos, H. B. (1971). Preparation of fractions of premelanosomes and melanosomes from pigmented S-91 melanomas. In: *Biology of Normal and Abnormal Melanocytes* (Kawamura, T., Fitzpatrick, T. B., and Seiji, M., eds.), pp. 515–24. University Park Press, Baltimore, London, Tokyo.

Fitzpatrick, T. B., Miyamoto, M., and Ishikawa, K. (1967). The evolution of concepts of melanin biology. In: *Advances in Biology of Skin,* Vol. 7 (Montagna, W., and Hu, F., eds.), pp. 1–30. Pergamon Press, New York.

Graham, R., Jr., and Karnovsky, M. (1966). Glomerular permeability: ultrastructural cytochemical studies using peroxidases as protein tracers. *J. Exp. Med.* **124**, 1123.

Hayat, M. A. (1970). *Principles and Techniques of Electron Microscopy: Biological Applications,* Vol. 1. Van Nostrand Reinhold Company, New York and London.

Hayat, M. A. (1972). *Basic Electron Microscopy Techniques.* Van Nostrand Reinhold Company, New York and London.

Hayat, M. A. (1973). Specimen preparation. In: *Electron Microscopy of Enzymes: Principles and Methods,* Vol. 1 (Hayat, M. A., ed.). Van Nostrand Reinhold Company, New York and London.

Hunter, J. A. A., Mottaz, J. H., and Zelickson, A. S. (1970). Melanogenesis: Ultrastructural histochemical observations on ultraviolet irradiated human melanocytes. *J. Invest. Dermatol.* **54**, 213.

Ide, C. (1972). The development of melanosomes in the pigment epithelium of the chick embryo. *Z. Zellforsch.* **131,** 171.

Lerner, A. B., Fitzpatrick, T. B., Calkins, E., and Summerson, W. H. (1949). Mammalian tyrosinase: preparation and properties. *J. Biol. Chem.* **178,** 185.

Maul, G. G., and Brumbaugh, J. A. (1971). On the possible function of coated vesicles in melanogenesis of the regenerating fowl feather. *J. Cell Biol.* **48,** 41.

Maul, G. G., and Romsdahl, M. M. (1970). Ultrastructural comparison of two malignant melanoma cell lines. *Cancer Res.* **30,** 2782.

Mishima, Y. (1964). Electron microscopic cytochemistry of melanosomes and mitochondria. *J. Histochem. Cytochem.* **12,** 784.

Novikoff, A. B., Albala, A., and Biampica, L. (1968). Ultrastructural and cytochemical observations on B16 and Harding-Passey mouse melanomas. The origin of premelanosomes and compound melanosomes. *J. Histochem. Cytochem.* **16,** 299.

Okun, M. R., Edelstein, L. M., Or, N., Hamada, G., Donnellan, B., and Lever, W. F. (1970). Histochemical differentiation of peroxidase-mediated from tyrosinate-mediated melanin formation in mammalian tissues: The biologic significance of peroxidase-mediated oxidation of tyrosinase to melanin. *Histochemie* **23,** 295.

Okun, M. R., Edelstein, L. M., Or, N., Hamada, G., Blumental, G., Donnellan, B., and Burnett, J. (1972). Oxidation of tyrosine and DOPA to melanin by mammalian peroxidase: The possible role of peroxidase in melanin synthesis and catecholamine synthesis *in vivo*. In: *Pigmentation: Its Genesis and Biologic Control* (Riley, V., ed.), p. 571. Appleton-Century-Crofts, New York.

Oliver, C., and Essner, E. (1972). Protein transport in mouse kidney utilizing tyrosinase as an ultrastructural tracer. *J. Exp. Med.* **136,** 291.

Pomerantz, S. H. (1966). The tyrosine hydroxylase activity of mammalian tyrosinase. *J. Biol. Chem.* **241,** 161.

Rodriguez, H. A., and McGavran, M. H. (1969). A modified DOPA reaction for the diagnosis and investigation of pigment cells. *Am. J. Clin. Path.* **52,** 219.

Seiji, M., Shimao, K., Birbeck, M. S. C., and Fitzpatrick, T. B. (1963). Subcellular localization of melanin biosynthesis. *Ann. N.Y. Acad. Sci.* **100,** 497.

Siakotos, A. N., Patel, V., and Cantaboni, A. (1973). The isolation and chemical composition of premelanosomes and melanosomes: Human and mouse melanomas. *Biochem. Med.* **7,** 14.

Stanka, P. (1970). Die Dopa-Reaktion, eine brauchbare Methode in der Elektronenmikroskopie. Untersuchung am retinalen Pigmentepithel von Hühnerembryonen. *Mikroskopie* **26,** 169.

Toda, K., and Fitzpatrick, T. B. (1971). The origin of melanosomes. In: *Biology of Normal and Abnormal Melanocytes* (Kawamura, T., Fitzpatrick, T. B., and Seiji, M., eds.), pp. 265–278. University Park Press, Baltimore, London, Tokyo.

Vogel, F. S., and McGregor, D. H. (1964). The fine structure and some biochemical correlates of melanogenesis in the ink gland of the squid. *Lab. Invest.* **13,** 767.

5

Sulfatases

VÄINÖ K. HOPSU-HAVU
AND HEIKKI HELMINEN

University of Turku, Turku, Finland

CLASSIFICATION OF SULFATASES

Sulfatases are enzymes which catalyze the hydrolytic cleavage of the anion of a sulfate ester according to the reaction equation $R \cdot OSO_3^- + H_2O \rightleftharpoons R \cdot OH + H^+ + SO_4^=$.

Sulfatases are commonly divided into several subclasses according to the chemical characteristics of the substrate hydrolyzed (Roy, 1971).

Arylsulfatases hydrolyze substrates in which $R \cdot OH$ is a phenol or one of its close derivatives.

Steroid sulfatases hydrolyze the sulfates of several steroids. Separate enzymes are considered to hydrolyze estrone sulfate, androsterone sulfate, etiocholanolone sulfate, and cortisone 21-sulfate.

Glycosulfatases hydrolyze various carbohydrate sulfates. Monosaccharide and disaccharide sulfates are split by glycosulfatases; complex sulfated glucans, by cellulose polysulfatase; and chondroitin sulfate and/or its degradation products, by chondrosulfatases.

Choline sulfatase hydrolyzes choline sulfate ester. This enzyme has been identified only in certain fungi and bacteria.

Alkylsulfatases hydrolyze alkyl sulfates. Separate enzymes hydrolyze the derivatives of primary and secondary alcohols. These enzymes are known to be present in bacteria, but have not been found in mammals.

Myrosulfatases appear to be a part of myrosinase, and hydrolyze oxime *o*-sulfonates. Their presence has been demonstrated in some plants and probably in mollusks, but not in mammals.

Other sulfohydrolases are present in animal tissues for the hydrolysis of 3'-phosphoadenylyl sulfate and adenylyl sulfate (Bailey-Wood *et al.,* 1969). Excellent biochemical reviews on sulfohydrolases, including methods for their study, are available (Roy, 1971; Dodgson and Spencer, 1957; Roy and Trudinger, 1970; Dodgson and Rose, 1970).

Arylsulfatases

From the point of view of ultrastructural localization, only arylsulfatases (arylsulfate sulfohydrolases, EC 3.1.6.1) are of practical interest. Therefore these will be dealt with in detail. They are also the only sulfatases which until now have been properly purified and characterized (Nicholls and Roy, 1971).

Type I arylsulfatases. Type I arylsulfatases are not inhibited by sulfate ions. They have been found in both microorganisms and animals. Arylsulfatase C of the mammalian liver belongs in this group. It has not been obtained in soluble form, and the preparations have always contained steroid sulfatase activity. This fact has been taken to indicate that arylsulfatase C has also some steroid sulfatase activity.

Type I sulfatases from *Aerobacter aerogenes* and *Aspergillus oryzae* are better known. The preferred substrates are 4-nitrophenyl sulfate, 2-nitrophenyl sulfate, and acetylphenyl sulfate; a general arylsulfatase substrate, 1-naphthylsulfate, as well as phenolphthalein disulfate, are hydrolyzed slowly. The pH optima of the Type I sulfatases are at pH 6 to 8.

Type II arylsulfatases. Type II arylsulfatases are characterized by being inhibited by sulfate ions. They are principally of animal origin, but have also been found in microorganisms. In the higher organisms, sulfatase A and B can be separated on the basis of several characteristics.

Sulfatase A, which has been purified from ox and human liver tissues, appears to be a fairly stable glycoprotein. It contains a large quantity of proline and has an acid isoelectric point. The molecular weight of the monomer form is 170,000. The enzyme may appear in monomer, dimer, or tetramer forms; the monomer is enzymatically most active. 2-Hydroxy-5-nitrophenyl sulfate, 3-nitrophenyl sulfate, 2-hydroxyphenyl and 2-nitrophenyl sulfates, and—interestingly—*p*-nitropyridyl 3-sulfate are preferably hydrolyzed. The pH optimum is at ~pH 5.0 to 5.5, but varies to some extent depending upon the conditions in the incubation medium. Sulfate and sulfite ions inhibit the enzyme competitively. The enzyme is also inhibited by carbonyl reagents and ascorbic acid in the presence of small amounts of metal ions, especially Cu^{2+}; however, this inhibition is hampered in the presence of EDTA.

Sulfatase B exists in two isozymic forms, which can be separated by chromatography on CM-Sephadex. It is present in a number of mammalian tissues, from which fairly pure preparations have been obtained.

Sulfatase B is clearly distinguished from sulfatase A by its alkaline isoelectric point and lower molecular weight. The substrate specificity of sulfatase B is approximately the same as that of sulfatase A. The hydrolysis of 4-nitrophenyl sulfate by the enzyme is activated by chloride, while the hydrolysis of other substrates is not. The inhibition of sulfatase B by sulfate ion is noncompetitive.

DISTRIBUTION AND SIGNIFICANCE OF SULFATASES

Arylsulfatases are widely distributed in mammalian organs. Sulfatases A and B are usually present in the same mammalian tissues, but their relative amounts may differ. In ox liver, sulfatase A is the principal enzyme; while in rat liver, sulfatase B is present in much higher amounts. Furthermore, liver fractions enriched in endothelial and Kupffer cells show a sulfatase A/B ratio considerably higher than the fractions enriched in parenchymal cells (Hook et al., 1970). The activity of arylsulfatase C is twice as high in the canine brain gray matter as in the white matter, while the total activity of arylsulfatases A and B is the same in these tissues (Clendenon and Allen, 1970).

Several less characterized sulfatases of Type II are present in invertebrate tissues and secretions. Satisfactory sources of sulfatases are juices of *Helix pomatia* (Dodgson and Powell, 1959) and *Proteus vulgaris* (Dodgson, 1959).

Tissue fractionation studies have shown that arylsulfatase C is a microsomal enzyme (Dodgson et al., 1957); it has been suggested as a microsomal marker enzyme in fractionation studies (Milson et al., 1968). Sulfatases A and B are found in a fraction of the heavier cell organelles identified as lysosomes (Viala and Gianetto, 1955; Bowers, 1969; Tappel, 1969; Barrett, 1969).

The exact biological significance of arylsulfatases is not known. It has been suggested (Mehl and Jatzkewitz, 1965 and 1968) that sulfatase A is involved in the degradation of cerebroside sulfate, and is a component of a more complex cerebroside sulfatase (Austin et al., 1964 and 1965). Extremely low activities were recorded in several organs (e.g., brain, kidney, and liver) of patients suffering from the inherited disease, metachromatic leucodystrophy. In similar conditions, Langelaan (1969) found low sulfatase A activities in leucocytes, and Porter *et al.* (1969) observed the same in cultured skin fibroblasts.

The natural substrate for sulfatase B is completely unknown. On the basis of histochemical studies, Leznicki and Bleszynski (1970) suggested that arylsulfatase A may be connected primarily with the nervous tract, while arylsulfatase B, hydrolyzing sulfuric esters of catecholamines, may be involved in the function of the drive system. The function of arylsulfatase C is also unknown, except for the suggested steroid sulfatase activity. Roy (1956) presented evidence that this enzyme is much more active in males than in females, and that it might also synthesize dehydroepiandrosterone sulfate.

According to Huggins and Smith (1947), *p*-nitrophenyl-sulfate hydrolyzing arylsulfatase activity of transferable rat sarcoma is $\sim$ 10 times higher than that of the connective tissue origin. Peripheral leucocytes in human myeloic leukaemia are known to have a high arylsulfatase activity, while those of lymphatic leukaemia are nearly devoid of it (Jibril *et al.*, 1972). A marked increase in the nitrocatechol sulfatase activity of the distal small intestine of the rat was recorded 5 to 16 days after birth (Danovitch and Laster, 1969). Treatment with ACTH or cortisone caused a marked decrease in the histochemically demonstrable arylsulfatase activity of the intestinal mucosa (Kilkowska-Chadzypanagiotis,1970). The significance of the above observations remains to be elucidated.

LOCALIZATION OF SULFATASES

Principles

In principle, the histochemical localization of sulfatase activity can be based on the visualization of either the anion or the cation liberated by the hydrolytic reaction. A prerequisite is that the ion to be demonstrated remains at the site of liberation as the consequence either of an immediate capture or of some other chemical reaction which results in an insoluble precipitate (Pearse, 1972).

Methods based on capture of the sulfate anion by heavy metal ions have yielded the best results. Both lead and barium ions have been used to obtain an insoluble heavy metal salt precipitate (Ohara and Kurata, 1952; Hopsu *et al.*, 1965, 1967; Goldfischer, 1965). The precipitate can be visualized by interference microscopy, by light microscopy after the conversion of lead sulfate into visible sulfide, or by using radioautography to detect radioactive sulfate (Kaviak *et al.*, 1964).

Selective demonstration of the site of the various arylsulfatases should be based on the differences in the substrate specificity of the sulfatases, since selective inhibitors are not currently known. The substrate of choice for the demonstration of arylsulfatase C would be 4-nitrophenyl sulfate, which is poorly hydrolyzed by arylsulfatases A and B (Roy, 1960). On the other hand, the latter enzymes readily hydrolyze nitrocatechol sulfates but hardly any 4-nitrophenyl sulfate. No strict histochemical differentiation is possible between sulfatases A and B on the basis of differences in their substrate specificity.

Methods based on the capture of the cation utilize the diazonium coupling of naphthol or 8-hydroxyquinoline liberated from the substrates. Sulfate esters of α- and β-naphthols have been used as substrates in simultaneous coupling reactions (Seligman et al., 1949), and those of 6-bromo or 6-benzoyl-2-naphthol, in a postcoupling reaction (Rutenburg et al., 1952). Naphthol AS (Gössner, 1958) and AS-D sulfates, as well as several of their derivatives (Woohsmann and Brosowski, 1964; Woohsmann and Hartrodt, 1964), have led to much improved histochemical techniques for the demonstration of arylsulfatase activity at the light microscope level. 8-Hydroxyquinoline sulfate has been used as the substrate with the concomitant use of barium as the capturing ion; 8-hydroxyquinoline coupled with hexazotized pararosanilin has also been utilized (Ohara and Kurata, 1952; Woohsmann and Hartrodt, 1967).

Electron microscopic methods for the localization of sulfatases are direct applications of the above methods based on anion capture by heavy metal ions.

Fixation

According to the prevailing view, glutaraldehyde is the fixative of choice in electron microscopic cytochemistry. The preservation of morphologic details after glutaraldehyde fixation is excellent, and in most cases, the recovery of enzymatic activity is sufficient to ensure proper demonstration of the site of the enzyme (Sabatini et al., 1963; Hayat, 1970 and 1973). Paraformaldehyde (2%, w/v) has also been used as the fixative, but its use has been limited compared to that of glutaraldehyde.

Glutaraldehyde fixation by perfusion or by immersion has been utilized in the stabilization of the ultrastructure. Purified glutaraldehyde solutions (1 to 3%, w/v) (purified either by redistillation or by repeated washing with active charcoal) have served as fixing agents (Anderson, 1967). Phosphate, cacodylate, veronal acetate, or Tris-maleate buffer at pH 7.4 (Hopsu-Havu et al., 1967; Goldfischer, 1965) often containing sucrose (1 to 2.5%; w/v) as well as dextran glucose (Seljelid and Helminen, 1968) have been used as the vehicles of the fixative. In addition, fixative solutions containing dimethyl sulfoxide (DMSO, 5%, w/v) have been utilized. It is well documented that DMSO facilitates the penetration of solutions and substrates into the tissue (Misch and Misch, 1967; Gander and Moppert, 1969; Hayat, 1973).

It is recognized that fixation of the tissue plays a key role in the electron microscopic demonstration of arylsulfatase activity (Goldfischer, 1965; Abraham, 1967; Ericsson and Helminen, 1967). The tissue should not be fixed either thoroughly or lightly, but the degree of fixation must be somewhere between the two extremes. Thorough perfusion fixation of the kidney tissue with glutaraldehyde well preserves the fine structure but abolishes most of the total arylsulfatase activity of the tissue. Arborgh et al. (1971) recorded a 70% loss of the activity after a thorough perfusion fixation. Hopsu-Havu et al. (1967), on the other hand, recorded a 22% loss of the arylsulfatase activity after a relatively brief immersion fixation; the enzyme could be readily demonstrated by cytochemical means after fixation. The discrepancy between these results can be explained only by the different modes of application of the fixative.

In general, although immersion fixation does not ensure excellent stabilization of the ultrastructure, all currently available data provide support for the utilization of this type of fixation in the demonstration of arylsulfatase activity. Ericsson and Helminen (1967) immersion-fixed whole kidneys with ligated vessels, and it was clearly shown that the optimal fixation of the tissue for enzyme histochemistry was achieved in a zone between the unfixed and well-preserved areas. Thus, the fixative first "opens" the membranes for the demonstration of arylsulfatase activity and later, when the fixation continues, it inactivates the enzyme. The area of optimal reaction can be chosen by using a light microscope, and then the same area of the section can be processed for electron microscopy. A proper standardization of the perfusion fixation has proved difficult in practice.

The results of Arborgh et al. (1971) prove unequivocally that rinsing of the tissues in buffer solutions restores some of the activity of arylsulfatase lost during fixation. Hence, it is appropriate to rinse tissue slices after fixation and prior to incubation for arylsulfatase. It is recommended that the tissues be rinsed in cold (4°C) buffer solutions (Hopsu-Havu et al., 1967; Ericsson and Helminen, 1967). Rinsing times may vary from 1 to 2 hr to 2 weeks. The purpose of rinsing is to remove the excess glutaraldehyde and the inhibitory ions from the tissue.

Frozen sections (40 to 50 μ thick), nonfrozen sections (50 to 200 μ thick) (Smith, 1970), or small tissue cubes (less than 1 mm^3) can be used for the demonstration of arylsulfatase activity. Before incubation, sections or cubes should be washed with a series (3 to 5) of buffer solutions (the same buffer as in the incubation medium).

Incubation

The incubation medium contains the substrate, buffer, and capturing ions. An ideal cytochemical method requires: (1) that the pH at the enzyme site is suitable for optimal enzyme activity; (2) that the enzyme is fully saturated with the substrate; and (3) that there are suitable capturing ions in excess around the active center of the enzyme molecule. Under these conditions, precise localization of the enzyme activity can be achieved.

In the demonstration of arylsulfatase activity at the subcellular level, 8-hydroxyquinoline sulfate and 2-hydroxy-5-nitrophenyl sulfate (*p*-nitrocatechol sulfate) have been used as the substrates (Table 5–1). Since *p*-nitrocatechol sulfate is more stable, "purer," and commercially available, it can be regarded at present as the most suitable substrate. Acetate, Veronal-acetate, Tris-HCL, and Tris-maleate buffers, at pH 4.2 to 7.0, have served as vehicles for the substrate (Hopsu-Havu *et al.,* 1967; Goldfischer, 1965). In principle, it can be stated: (1) that the buffer should

Table 5–1   Papers Dealing with the Demonstration of Arylsulfatase Activity at the Electron Microscopic Level

Tissue, Animal	Substrate and Capturing Ion	Location	Reference
Brain, rat	NCS	Lysosomes	Goldfischer, 1965
Kidney, rat	NCS, 8-hydroxy-quinoline sulfate, lead and barium	Lysosomes	Hopsu et al., 1965; Goldfischer, 1965; Hopsu-Havu et al., 1967; Ericsson and Helminen, 1967
Liver, rat	NCS, lead	Lysosomes	Abraham, 1967
Heart, rat	NCS, lead	Lysosomes	Abraham et al., 1967
Duodenum, rat	NCS, barium	Lysosomes	Hugon and Borgers, 1967
Epidermis, human	NCS, lead and barium	Lysosomes	Olson et al., 1968
Mammary gland, rat	NCS, lead and barium	Lysosomes	Helminen et al., 1968
Leucocytes, rabbit and rat	NCS, lead and barium	Lysosomes, Golgi complex and endoplasmic reticulum	Bainton and Farquhar, 1968; Bainton and Farquhar, 1970
Lung, rat	NCS, barium	Lysosomes	Corrin and Clark, 1968
Thyroid, rat	NCS, lead	Lysosomes	Seljelid and Helminen, 1968
Retina, rat	NCS, lead	Lysosomes	Abraham et al., 1969
Thymus, rat	NCS, barium	Lysosomes	Ökrös et al., 1969
Uterus, rat	NCS, lead	Lysosomes	Carlsöö and Bloom, 1969
Bone epiphysis, guinea pig	NCS, lead	Dense bodies, Golgi complex, matrix vesicles, Type I	Thyberg, 1972

not form a complex or precipitate with the substrate or capturing ion, and (2) that it should not inhibit the enzyme activity.

The above-mentioned points also hold true for the capturing ions. Barium chloride appears to be almost ideal in this respect. It seldom forms precipitates in the incubation solutions and does not inhibit the enzyme (Hopsu-Havu et al., 1967). Lead ions, on the contrary, readily form precipitates and, in relatively low concentrations, inhibit the function of the enzyme, although not at the concentration employed in the incubation media (Hopsu-Havu et al., 1967; Leznicki and Bleszynski, 1970). For light microscopy, many investigators prefer the use of lead nitrate over that of barium chloride for the demonstration of arylsulfatase activity. This is apparently due to the fact that the lead sulfate precipitate is easily converted into black sulfide which is visible in the light microscope.

The following two incubation media have been generally utilized in the demonstration of arylsulfatase activity:

Method Proposed by Goldfischer (1965)

p-nitrocatechol sulfate	15 to 30 mg
Veronal-acetate buffer (pH 5.4)	5.0 ml
Lead nitrate (24%)	0.16 ml

The pH should be adjusted to the desired value.

Method by Hopsu-Havu et al. (1967)

p-nitrocatechol sulfate in 3 ml distilled H_2O	120 mg
Acetate buffer (0.1 M), pH 5.5	9.0 ml
Barium chloride (5%)	3.0 ml
or	
Lead nitrate (8%)	3.0 ml

The pH should be adjusted to 5.0 to 5.5 with a few drops of 0.2 M acetic acid.

In the second method, the effect of different concentrations of the substrate and capturing ions on arylsulfatase activity has been tested by both biochemical and histochemical means. It appears that in the second incubation medium, the enzyme is properly saturated with the substrate. Furthermore, the inhibitory effect of lead nitrate is of minor significance (less than 10%, depending upon the amount of protein in the medium). Simultaneously, the effect of $BaCl_2$ on arylsulfatase activity is negligible in the incubation medium (5% solution). Recommended incubation durations range from 5 to 10 min to 90 min at 37°C.

Processing of the Tissue for Electron Microscopy

After incubation, the sections are rinsed in 3 to 5 consecutive changes of buffer solution containing 5 to 7.5% sucrose. The sections can be further fixed either with buffered glutaraldehyde (see above) or with osmium tetroxide (1 to 2%, w/v), buffered to pH 7.3 with an appropriate buffer (e.g., s-collidine). In principle, the time of postfixation should be restricted to the minimum, since prolonged immersion can cause diffusion of the reaction product in the tissue. The sections are then taken through a graded series of ethanol solutions, propylene oxide, and embedded in Epon according to the procedures described in detail by Hayat (1970, 1972, and 1973). During dehydration, the tissues can be stained *en bloc* with 2% uranyl acetate dissolved in absolute alcohol. After the polymerization of the embedding medium, thin sections, 400 to 900 Å in thickness, are cut with an ultramicrotome. Both unstained sections and sections double-stained with uranyl acetate and lead citrate are examined by electron microscopy.

Thick sections (1 to 2 μ), for the demonstration of arylsulfatase activity by light microscopy, can also be prepared (Ericsson and Helminen, 1967; Seljelid and Helminen, 1968). For this purpose, tissues should be taken through dilute $(NH_4)_2S$ solution (1 to 2%, w/v) after the incubation and rinsing procedures. By counterstaining these sections with toluidine blue, the distribution of reaction product can be related to cytologic structure.

Controls

The following three controls should be included in the procedure: (1) Some of the sections should be incubated in a medium lacking the substrate. (2) Some incubated sections should not be postfixed in osmium tetroxide (but only with glutaraldehyde or paraformaldehyde). (3) The thin sections obtained from group 2 tissues should be examined without lead and uranyl acetate counter staining, since changes in the precipitate may occur during such heavy metal staining (Kalimo *et al.,* 1968).

Location of Arylsulfatase Activity

Arylsulfatase activity has been demonstrated in many different tissues and cells. A comprehensive list of articles concerning the demonstration of arylsulfatase activity is presented in Table 5–1. This table may be of help in establishing a precise cytochemical method. Examples of the results are given in Figs. 5–1 and 5–2 at the light microscopic level and in Figs. 5–3 and 5–4 at the electron microscopic level.

Considering the data presented above, it is concluded that arylsulfatase is located in lysosomes. Most workers agree with this view. The cytochemical observations are corroborated with biochemical results, which unequivocally show that in differential and gradient centrifugation experiments, arylsulfatases A and B are sedimented in the lysosomal fraction (Bowers, 1969; Tappel, 1969; Barrett, 1969). Thus, it appears that the lysosomal origin of these arylsulfatases is indisputable. Similarly, all lysosomes may not be equal as to their enzyme content, since all lysosomes, even in the same cell, do not seem to contain demonstrable arylsulfatase activity (Pfeifer, 1969; Ericsson and Helminen, 1967).

The electron cytochemical demonstration of final reaction product in lysosomes, Golgi cisternae, vesicles, and vacuoles, and occasionally in cisternae of the endoplasmic reticulum (Bainton and Farquhar, 1968 and 1970) supports the view that arylsulfatase molecules are synthesized on/at the ribosomes and transported through the endoplasmic reticulum to the Golgi area, where the enzyme molecules are concentrated (Palade, 1966). Furthermore, according to the same view, "primary" lysosomes derived from the Golgi apparatus (de Duve and Wattiaux, 1966) or GERL (Novikoff et al., 1971) take the newly formed enzyme from the Golgi area to the "secondary" lysosomes. The scheme presented above appears plausible, but verification awaits intracellular enzyme turnover studies.

On the other hand, occasional deposits of final reaction product in some parts of the nucleus, nucleolus, mitochondria, plasma membrane and brush border, basement lamina, and diffusely throughout the cytoplasma are at present considered artificial (Kalimo et al., 1967; Arstila et al., 1967). It is the prevailing view that false sites of enzyme activity are due to an inadequate fixation and a consequence of unsuitable processing of the tissues during incubation, rinsing, or staining.

Comments on the Method

In practice, the method for the electron microscopic demonstration of arylsulfatase activity has proved to be somewhat capricious. Sometimes the reaction is easy to carry out, but on other occasions no results are obtained at all. We are convinced that fixation and inhibitory ions in the incubation medium are the crucial factors that govern the yield of successful or unsuccessful results. Frozen, unfixed sections do not yield any reaction for arylsulfatase, and a thorough fixation of the tissue also abolishes enzyme activity. Brief perfusion of the tissue with aldehyde fixatives often yields a "spotty" arylsulfatase reaction. Hence, we recommend immersion fixation of relatively large tissue blocks.

In frozen sections prepared from these tissues, the frontier of the penetration of fixative can be identified, as well as the appearance of arylsulfatase reaction at various depths in the fixed tissue (Ericsson and Helminen,

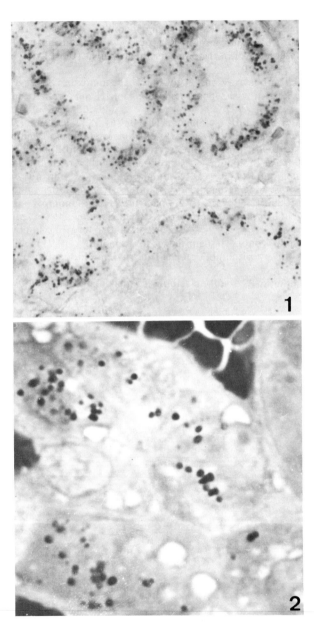

Fig. 5–1. Light microscopic demonstration of arylsulfatase activity in renal proximal tubule cells. Glutaraldehyde immersion fixation, frozen section, incubation time 30 min. ×400.

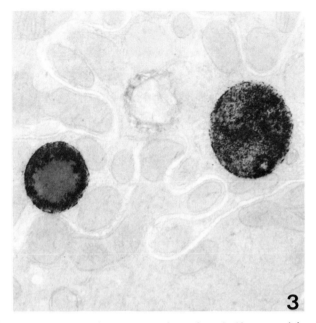

Fig. 5-3. Electron microscopic demonstration of arylsulfatase activity in a renal proximal tubule cell. The black deposits over the two lysosome-like bodies mark the site of the enzyme activity. Glutaraldehyde immersion, unstained section. X24,000.

1967). This "reactive" area can be dissected free under the light microscope, postfixed, and then processed for electron microscopy. Of course the difficulties described above may be overcome, at least in part, by "mild" perfusion fixation of the tissue with glutaraldehyde or paraformaldehyde. However, in practice, the meaning of the term "mild" has to be established empirically for each tissue type.

The second deleterious factor is the presence of inhibitory ions in the incubation medium. It has been shown that many ions inhibit arylsulfatase activity (Barrett, 1969). Among them are phosphate, sulfate, cacodylate, and lead ions. Thus, it is of utmost importance to rinse the sections thoroughly in Veronal acetate buffer before incubation, and to prepare the incubation medium correctly. However, barium and chloride ions, in the concentration utilized in the experiments, do not significantly inhibit the enzyme (Hopsu-Havu *et al.*, 1967; Leznicki and Bleszynski, 1970).

It has been shown (Fig. 5-4) that the heavy metal precipitates found over the lysosomes are barium or lead sulfate (Arstila *et al.*, 1966; Pfeifer,

Fig. 5-2. Light microscopic demonstration of arylsulfatase activity in renal proximal tubule cells. Glutaraldehyde immersion fixation, toluidine blue staining, incubation time 60 min. X1500.

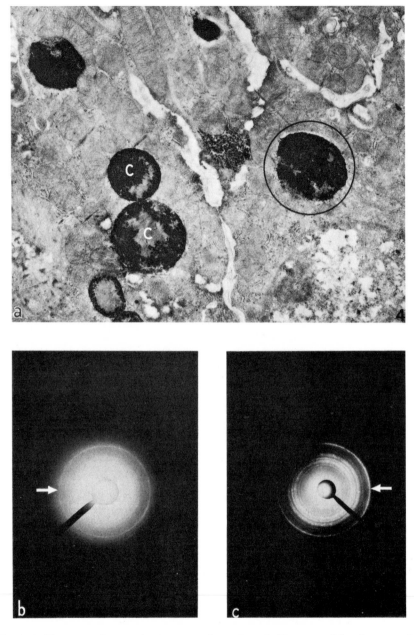

Fig. 5–4. Electron microscopic demonstration of arylsulfatase activity in a renal proximal tubule cell. Barium has been used as the capturing ion. The lysosome encircled was selected for microdiffraction (Fig. 5–4a, ×19,000). The diffraction pattern of the lysosome containing final reaction product is depicted in Fig. 5–4b. The outer-

1969). While these precipitates are highly insoluble, some reaction product can be dissolved in the processing of the tissue, as seen in Fig. 5–5 (Kalimo *et al.,* 1968; Bainton and Farquhar, 1968). The dissolution of barium sulfate from thin sections can be prevented by staining the section with solutions that are saturated with $BaSO_4$ (Kalimo *et al.,* 1968). At the same time, the disappearance of lead sulfate from the sections can be avoided by treating the incubated tissues with $(NH_4)_2S$. Ammonium sulfide converts lead sulfate into lead sulfide, which is more suitable for electron microscopy (Bainton and Farquhar, 1968). Leaching of lead sulfate from ultrathin sections can also occur during lead citrate staining (Kalimo *et al.,* 1968).

When considering the substrate specificity and other enzymatic characteristics of arylsulfatases, one would expect that arylsulfatases A and B are primarily demonstrated by the above methods. A differential demonstration of these enzymes was claimed by Goldfischer (1965) based on differences in the pH optima of the enzymes: a reaction at pH 4.2 was considered to be suitable for arylsulfatase A, and at pH 5.5 to be optimal for arylsulfatase B. Such a differentiation was not, however, considered possible by Hopsu-Havu *et al.* (1967) and Leznicki and Bleszynski (1970), because the pH curves of these enzymes overlap.

Recommended Method

(1) Fix relatively large tissue blocks in 3% purified glutaraldehyde, buffered with 0.1 M cacodylate or Tris-maleate buffer, pH 7.4.

(2) Prepare frozen sections (40 to 50 μ thick) or nonfrozen sections (50 to 200 μ thick).

(3) Rinse the sections in 3 consecutive solutions of acetate buffer (Veronal-acetate), pH 5.5.

(4) Incubate the sections in one of the two media given on p. 97 for 10 to 90 min.

(5) Rinse the sections in 3 to 5 consecutive solutions of acetate (or Veronal-acetate) buffer, pH 5.5.

(6) Postosmicate some of the sections; postfix the other sections in glutaraldehyde or paraformaldehyde.

(7) Dehydrate and prepare thin sections for electron microscopy.

(8) To each of the solutions mentioned above, add sucrose (concentration 1 to 7.5%).

---

most intense ring (arrow) was used in the identification of the precipitate. Fig. 5–4c, demonstrates the diffraction pattern of the standard specimen of crystalline barium sulfate. The diffraction pattern proves unequivocally that the reaction product found over lysosomes is $BaSO_4$. The ring corresponding to that marked in Fig. 5–4b is marked with an arrow. From Arstila *et al.* (1966).

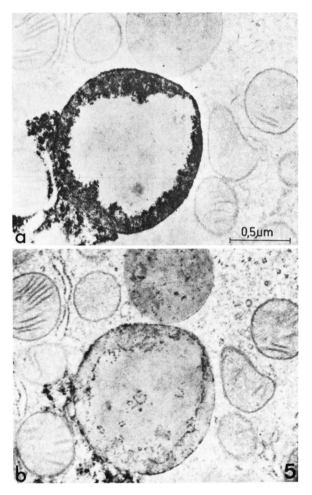

Fig. 5–5. Arylsulfatase activity demonstrated as barium sulfate. (a). No counter staining. (b). Staining with lead citrate for 5 min. Note the loss of reaction product. From Kalimo *et al.* (1968).

CONCLUSIONS

The methods discussed above demonstrate predominantly arylsulfatases of Type II. Electron microscopic demonstration of sulfatases thus remains at present limited to a small part of the numerous sulfatases distinctly characterized by biochemical means. In principle, the metal ion precipitation techniques should be applicable for demonstration of other sulfatases of animal as well as of plant origin. Selection of the substrate to fit the specificity of the enzyme should allow demonstration of other sulfatases, with the presumption that the enzymes can survive the treatments required for their fixation *in situ* in the tissue. In fact, attempts have been made to demonstrate arylsulfatase C (Kaviak *et al.,* 1964) by using *p*-nitrophenyl sulfate and myrosulfatase (Ohara and Kurata, 1950) by using sinigrin as a substrate at the light microscopic level.

Similar attempts to demonstrate mammalian chondrosulfatase using heparin and chondroitin sulfate as substrates have not been unsuccessful (Dohlman and Friedenwald, 1955). Naturally, demonstration of the enzyme activity is difficult at the electron microscopic level if the light microscopic results are negative.

Perhaps further distinction between the enzymes demonstrated by the available methods can be achieved in the future when more specific substrates and enzyme modifiers are available. For instance, the differences in the location between arylsulfatases A and B should be thoroughly researched.

So far the application of the available methods has lead to verification of the site of arylsulfatases at the level of cell organelles. Electron microscopy reveals the activity of Type II arylsulfatases in lysosomal organelles, while biochemical studies reveal its presence in major organelles, together with several lysosomal enzymes. When interpreting the results, it should, however, be kept in mind that a lack of reaction product at any tissue site does not necessarily mean a lack of enzyme activity at that site.

Further studies may reveal other enzyme locations in tissues. They may also throw additional light on the synthesis and metabolism of cellular sulfatases and on the function of the organelles involved in the synthesis and storage of cellular macromolecules. Considerable differences may exist between mammalian tissues and lower organisms in which arylsulfatases are present—for instance, in secretory and digestive fluids. In the field of human pathology, the problems of storage diseases—for example, those of metachromatic leucodystrophy, a disease of arylsulfatase deficiency—remain to be elucidated. In these studies, the combined use of conventional electron microscopy and electron cytochemistry should prove to be of utmost importance in unraveling the pathophysiology of the diseases.

REFERENCES

Abraham, R. (1967). Lysosomal arylsulphatase in the liver. *Histochemie* **11,** 129.

Abraham, R., Hume, M., and Smith, L. (1969). A histochemical study of lysosomal enzymes in the retina of the rat. *Histochemie* **18,** 195.

Abraham, R., Morris, M., and Smith, J. (1967). Histochemistry of lysosomes in rat heart muscle. *J. Histochem. Cytochem.* **15**, 596.

Anderson, P. J. (1967). Purification and quantitation of glutaraldehyde and its effect in several enzyme activities. In skeletal muscle. *J. Histochem. Cytochem.* **15**, 652.

Arborgh, B., Ericsson, J. L. E., and Helminen, H. J. (1971). Inhibition of renal acid phosphatase and aryl sulfatase activity by glutaraldehyde fixation. *J. Histochem. Cytochem.* **19**, 499.

Arstila, A. U., Helminen, H. J., and Kalimo, H. (1967). Possible sources of error in demonstrating aryl sulfatase. I. Incubation and post-osmication. *J. Ultrastruct. Res.* **20**, 294.

Arstila, A. U., Jaakkola, S., Kalimo, H., Helminen, H. J., and Hopsu-Havu, V. K. (1966). Electron diffraction as the control of enzyme histochemical reactions at the ultrastructural level. *J. Microscopie* **5**, 777.

Austin, J., Armstrong, J., and Shearer, L. (1965). Metachromic form of diffuse cerebral sclerosis. *Archs. Neurol.* **13**, 593.

Austin, K., McAfee, D., Armstrong, D., O'Rourke, M., Shearer, L., and Bachawat, B. (1964). Abnormal sulfatase activity in two human diseases (metachromatic leucodystrophy and gargoylism). *Biochem. J.* **93**, 15c.

Bailey-Wood, R., Dodgson, K. S., and Rose, F. A. (1969). A rat liver sulphohydrolase enzyme acting on adenylyl sulphate. *Biochem. J.* **112**, 257.

Bainton, D. F., and Farquhar, M. G. (1968). Differences in enzyme content of azurophil and specific granules of polymorphonuclear leukocytes. II. Cytochemistry and electron microscopy of bone marrow cells. *J. Cell Biol.* **39**, 299.

Bainton, D. F., and Farquhar, M. G. (1970). Segregation and packaging of granule enzymes in eosinophilic leukocytes. *J. Cell Biol.* **45**, 54.

Barrett, A. J. (1969). Properties of lysosomal enzymes. In: *Lysosomes in Biology and Pathology* (Dingle, J. T., and Fell, H. B., eds.), Vol. 2, p. 245. North-Holland Publishing Co., Amsterdam.

Bowers, W. E. (1969). Lysosomes in lymphoid tissues: Spleen, thymus, and lymph nodes. In: *Lysosomes in Biology and Pathology* (Dingle, J. T., and Fell, H. B., eds.), Vol. I, p. 167. North-Holland Publishing Co., Amsterdam.

Carlsöö, B., and Bloom, G. D. (1969). Intracellular localization of acid phosphatase and arylsulfatase in rat metrial gland cells. *Experientia* **25**, 1068.

Clendenon, N. R., and Allen, N. (1970). Assay and subcellular localization of the arylsulfatases in rat brain. *J. Neurochem.* **17**, 865.

Corrin, B., and Clark, A. E. (1968). Lysosomal arylsulphatase in pulmonary alveolar cell. *Histochemie* **15**, 95.

Danovitch, S. H., and Laster, L. (1969). The development of arylsulphatase in the small intestine of the rat. *Biochem. J.* **114**, 343.

Dodgson, K. S. (1959). Observations on the arylsulphatase of *Proteus vulgaris*. *Enzymologia* **20**, 301.

Dodgson, K. S., and Powell, G. M. (1959). Studies on sulphates. 27. The purification and properties of the arylsulphatase of the digestive gland of *Helix pomatia*. *Biochem. J.* **73**, 672.

Dodgson, K. S., and Rose, F. A. (1970). In: *Metabolic Conjugation and Metabolic Hydrolysis* (Fishman, W. H., ed.), Vol. 1, p. 239. Academic Press, New York.

Dodgson, K. S., Rose, F. A., and Spencer, B. (1957). Studies on sulphatases. 16. A soluble preparation of arylsulphatase C of rat-liver microsomes. *Biochem. J.* **66**, 357.

Dodgson, K. S., and Spencer, B. (1957). Assay of sulphatases. *Methods Biochem. Anal.* **4,** 211.

Dohlman, C-H., and Friedenwald, J. S. (1955). Pitfalls in histochemistry: An unsuccessful attempt to demonstrate mucoid sulfatase activity in mammalian tissue. *J. Histochem. Cytochem.* **3,** 492.

de Duve, C., and Wattiaux, R. (1966). Functions of lysosomes. *Ann. Rev. Physiol.* **28,** 435.

Ericsson, J. L. E., and Helminen, H. J. (1967). Observations on the localization of arylsulphatase activity in renal cortical tubules. *Histochemie* **9,** 170.

Gander, E. S., and Moppert, J. M. (1969). Der Einfluss von Dimethylsulfoxid auf die Permeabilität der Lysosomenmembran bei quantitativer und qualitativer Darstellung der sauren Phosphatase. *Histochemie* **20,** 211.

Goldfischer, S. (1965). The cytochemical demonstration of lysosomal aryl sulfatase activity by light and electron microscopy. *J. Histochem. Cytochem.* **13,** 520.

Gössner, W. (1958). Histochemischer Nachweis hydrolytischer Enzyme mit Hilfe der Azofarbstoffmethode. *Histochemie* **1,** 48.

Hayat, M. A. (1970). *Principles and Techniques of Electron Microscopy. Biological Applications,* Vol. I, p. 93. Van Nostrand Reinhold Company, New York and London.

Hayat, M. A. (1972). *Basic Electron Microscopy Techniques.* Van Nostrand Reinhold Company, New York and London.

Hayat, M. A. (1973). Specimen preparation. In: *Electron Microscopy of Enzymes: Principles and Methods,* Vol. I (Hayat, M. A., ed.). Van Nostrand Reinhold Company, New York and London.

Helminen, H. J., Ericson, J. L. E., and Orrenius, S. (1968). Studies of mammary gland involution. IV. Histochemical and biochemical observations on alterations in lysosomes and lysosomal enzymes. *J. Ultrastruct. Res.* **25,** 240.

Hook, G. E. R., Dodgson, K. S., and Rose, F. A. (1970). Lysosomal arylsulfatases A and B of rat liver. *Biochem. J.* **119.**

Hopsu, V. K., Arstila, A. V., and Glenner, G. G. (1965). A method for electron microscopic localization of arylsulphatase. *Ann. Med. Exp. Biol. Fenn.* **43,** 114.

Hopsu-Havu, V. K., Arstila, A. V., Helminen, H. J., and Kalimo, H. O. (1967). Improvements in the method for the electron microscopic localization of arylsulphatase activity. *Histochemie* **8,** 54.

Hugon, J., and Borgers, M. (1967). Fine structural localization of lysosomal enzymes in the absorbing cells of the duodenal mucosa of the mouse. *J. Cell Biol.* **33,** 212.

Huggins, C., and Smith, D. R. (1947). Chromogenic substrates. III. *p*-Nitrophenyl sulfate as a substrate for the assay of phenolsulfatase activity. *J. Biol. Chem.* **170,** 391.

Jibril, A. O., Sawalha, S., and Volini, F. I. (1972). Leukocyte enzyme methods in the differential diagnosis of leukemia. *Clin. Chem.* **18,** 704.

Kalimo, H. O., Arstila, A. V., Helminen, H., and Hopsu-Havu, V. K. (1967). Possible sources of error in demonstrating aryl sulfatase. II. Staining. *J. Ultrastruct. Res.* **20,** 295.

Kalimo, H., Helminen, H. J., Arstila, A. V., and Hopsu-Havu, V. K. (1968). The loss of enzyme reaction products from ultrathin sections during staining for electron microscopy. *Histochemie* **14,** 123.

Kaviak, J., Sawicki, W., and Miks, B. (1964). Histochemical reaction on aryl-sulfatase C activity. *Acta Histochem.* **19**, 184.

Kilkowska-Chadzypanagiotis, K. (1970). The effect of ACTH and cortisone on behavior of arylsulfatase in intestinal mucosa of white rat. *Acta Histochem.* **38**, 305.

Langelaan, D. E. (1969). Leucocyte arylsulphatase in metachromatic leucodystrophy. *Biochem. J.* **112**, 26 p.

Leznicki, A., and Bleszynski, W. (1970). Histochemical localization of the soluble arylsulfatase activities in rat brain. *Histochemie* **24**, 251.

Mehl, E., and Jatzkewitz, H. (1965). Evidence for the genetic block in metachromatic leucodystrophy. *Biochem. Biophys. Res. Commun.* **19**, 407.

Mehl, E., and Jatzkewitz, H. (1968). Cerebroside 3-sulfate as a physiological substrate of arylsulfatase A. *Biochim. Biophys. Acta* **515**, 619.

Milson, D. W., Rose, F. A., and Dodgson, K. S. (1968). Assay of a microsomal marker enzyme: Rat liver arylsulphatase C. *Biochem. J.* **109**.

Misch, D. W., and Misch, S. M. (1967). Dimethyl sulfoxide: Activation of lysosomes in vitro. *Proc. Nat. Acad. Sci.* **58**, 2463.

Nicholls, R. G., and Roy, A. B. (1971). Arylsulfatase. In: *The Enzymes* (Boyer, P. D., ed.), Vol. I, 3d ed., p. 21. Academic Press, New York, London.

Novikoff, P. M., Novikoff, A. B., Quintana, N., and Hauw, J.-J. (1971). Golgi apparatus, GERL, and lysosomes of neurons in rat dorsal root ganglia, studied by thick section and thin section cytochemistry. *J. Cell Biol.* **50**, 859.

Ohara, M., and Kurata, J. (1950). Cited by Pearse, 1972.

Ohara, M., and Kurata, J. (1952). Cited by Pearse, 1972.

Ökrös, I., Fazekas, I., Bacsy, E., Rappay, G., and Toro, I. (1969). Hydrolytic enzyme activity of rat thymic cells grown in vitro. *Histochemie* **20**, 108.

Olson, R. L., Nordquist, J., and Everett, M. A. (1968). Ultrastructural localization of aryl sulfatase in human epidermis. *Acta Dermatovener* (Stockholm) **48**, 556.

Palade, G. E. (1966). Structure and function at the cellular level. *J. Amer. Med Ass.* **198**, 815.

Pearse, A. G. E. (1972). *Histochemistry, Theoretical and Applied,* Vol. II, 3d ed., p. 987. Churchill Livingstone, Edinburgh and London.

Pfeifer, U. (1969). Kombinierte elektronmikroskopische Darstellung der Aryl-sulfatase und der sauren Phosphatase in Lysosomen des Nierentubulus. *Histochemie* **17**, 284.

Porter, M. T., Fluharty, A. L., and Kihara, H. (1969). Metachromatic leuko-dystrophy: Arylsulfatase—A deficiency in skin fibroblast cultures. *Proc. Nat. Acad. Sci.* **62**, 887.

Roy, A. B. (1956). The enzymic synthesis of steroid sulfates. *Biochem. J.* **63**, 294.

Roy, A. B. (1960). The synthesis and hydrolysis of sulfate esters. *Adv. Enzymol.* **22**, 205.

Roy, A. B. (1971). The hydrolysis of sulfate esters. In: *The Enzymes,* (Boyer, P. D., ed), Vol. V, 3d ed., p. 1. Academic Press, New York and London.

Roy, A. B., and Trudinger, P. A. (1970). *The Biochemistry of Inorganic Compounds of Sulfur.* Cambridge University Press, London and New York.

Rutenburg, A. M., Cohen, R. B., and Seligman, A. M. (1952). Histochemical demonstration of aryl sulfatase. *Science* **116**, 539.

Sabatini, D. D., Bensch, K., and Barrnett, R. J. (1963). Cytochemistry and electron microscopy. The preservation of cellular structure and enzymatic activity by aldehyde fixation. *J. Cell Biol.* **17,** 19.

Seligman, A. M., Nachlas, M. M., Manheimer, L. H., Friedman, O. M., and Wolf, G. (1949). Development of new methods for the histochemical demonstration of hydrolytic intracellular enzymes in a program of cancer research. *Ann. Surg.* **130,** 333.

Seljelid, R., and Helminen, H. J. (1968). The localization of arylsulfatase activity in thyroid follicle cells. *J. Histochem. Cytochem.* **16,** 467.

Smith, R. E. (1970). Comparative evaluation of two instruments and procedures to cut nonfrozen sections. *J. Histochem. Cytochem.* **18,** 590.

Tappel, A. L. (1969). Lysosomal enzymes and other components. In: *Lysosomes in Biology and Pathology* (Dingle, J. T., and Fell, H. B., eds.), Vol. II, p. 207. North-Holland Publishing Co., Amsterdam.

Thyberg, J. (1972). Ultrastructural localization of arylsulphatase activity in the epiphyseal plate. *J. Ultrastruct. Res.* **38,** 332.

Viala, R., and Gianetto, R. (1955). The binding of sulphatase by rat-liver particles as compared to that of acid phosphatase. *Can. J. Biochem. Physiol.* **33,** 839.

Woohsmann, H., and Brosowski, K. H. (1964). Über den topochemischen Nachweis einer Naphthol-C-Sulfatase im Zentralnervensystem der Ratte. *Acta histochem.* **18,** 179.

Woohsmann, H., and Hartrodt, W. (1964). Der Nachweis einer Phosphatempfindlichen Sulfatase mit Naphthol-AS-Sulfaten. *Histochemie* **4,** 336.

Woohsmann, H., and Hartrodt, W. (1967). Der lichtmikroskopische Nachweis der Arylsulfatase mit 8-Oxychinolinsulfat. *Histochemie* **11,** 81.

6

Adenylate Cyclase

ROGER C. WAGNER
AND MARK W. BITENSKY

Departments of Anatomy and Pathology, Yale University Medical School, New Haven, Connecticut

INTRODUCTION

Many hormones produce specific responses in cells by changing the intracellular concentration of cyclic AMP, and they do so by controlling the activity of the enzyme adenylate cyclase (3.6.1.8). In most instances, the interaction of a hormone with cyclase involves the binding of the hormone to a specific receptor site on the outer surface of the plasma membrane. This activates cyclase, which then generates cyclic AMP from ATP at a catalytic site on the cytoplasmic side of the plasma membrane (Bitensky and Gorman, 1972). Altered levels of cyclic AMP in the cytoplasm then elicit the cellular responses once attributed to the action of hormones exclusively. In this regard, cyclic AMP has become distinguished as the "second messenger" (Sutherland *et al.,* 1968; Robison *et al.,* 1968).

Adenyl cyclase is associated with the cells of almost all mammalian tissues, and a great deal of information has been compiled about its operational specificity for hormones (Butcher *et al.,* 1972). Such ubiquity attests to the universality of cyclase as a component of plasma membranes and to the ability of many cell types to respond to extracellular effectors by altering intracellular levels of cyclic AMP.

Cyclase activity has been primarily associated with plasma membrane fractions (Davoren and Sutherland, 1963; Pohl *et al.,* 1969), but it has not been possible to discern whether it functions over the entire surface of cell or is discontinuous and localized, for instance, on that portion of a cell's surface facing a lumen. Complications arise from the cellular heterogeneity of tissues such as liver and adipose, and different cell types within a tissue may exhibit distinguishable hormone sensitivities. Little is known about cyclase activity within the cell and its existence in intracellular membranes. A cytochemical technique for ultrastructurally localizing cyclase is therefore: (1) a beneficial adjunct procedure for corroborating biochemical determinations, (2) an effective method for analyzing the distribution of this enzyme among different cell types within a tissue and within intracellular membrane systems, and (3) a means of detecting discontinuity of cyclase activity along the surface of the plasma membrane.

GENERAL PROCEDURES

Substrates

Adenyl cyclase is a phosphatase which hydrolyzes ATP to cyclic AMP and pyrophosphate (PP_i). Various phosphatases such as ATPases (3.6.1.3) and 5'-nucleotidase (3.1.3.5) have been localized on the plasma membrane of cells by precipitating lead as the salt of pyrophosphate or inorganic phosphate (P_i) (Essner, 1973). Since these are the products of many phosphatase reactions, the specificity of such determinations resides in the use of specific substrates for the enzyme sought.

ATP serves as a substrate for both adenyl cyclase and other ATPases, and in standard Wachstein-Meisel phosphatase determinations (1957), both PP_i and P_i will precipitate as an electron-dense lead salt.

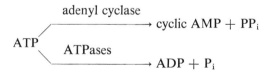

Thus ATP does not discriminate between the presence of ATPases and adenyl cyclase in procedures involving precipitation of reaction products with lead.

Specificity may be enhanced by the use of a substrate which is hydrolyzed by cyclase but not by other ATPases. Such a substrate is the compound 5'-adenylyl-imidodiphosphate (AMP-PNP), which was first synthesized by Yount and collaborators (1971) and is now available from I.C.N., Irvine, California. Various investigators (Rodbell *et al.,* 1971; Krishna *et al.,*

1972; Howell and Whitfield, 1972) have shown that AMP-PNP serves as an effective substrate for adenyl cyclase, resulting in the products cyclic AMP and imidodiphosphate (PNP). It is not hydrolyzed by the usual group of membrane ATPases, however, presumably because these enzymes are not able to cleave the imido bond joining the two terminal phosphates. The product PNP, which is formed from the activity of adenyl cyclase, will precipitate with lead to form an electron-dense marker.

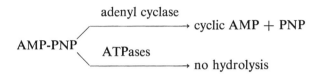

The use of the specific cyclase substrate AMP-PNP therefore simplifies interpretation of the enzymic source of the reaction product by precluding formation of lead phosphate through the action of ATPases. Although other enzymes can utilize AMP-PNP as a substrate, none of these are known to be membrane-associated.*

Intracellular cyclic AMP is continuously degraded to 5' AMP by cyclic AMP phosphodiesterase (Sutherland and Rall, 1958). This is potentially a source of contaminating reaction product since 5'-nucleotidases can further degrade 5' AMP to adenosine and P_i, which will precipitate as a lead salt. A reaction medium for localizing cyclase must therefore include a phosphodiesterase (3.1.4.1) inhibitor such as the methylxanthines, theophylline, or aminophylline (Butcher and Sutherland, 1962). The inhibitor must be present in sufficient quantities to completely inhibit the conversion of cyclic AMP to 5'AMP.

Incubation Conditions

The reaction medium should be buffered close to the 7.4 pH optimum of cyclase (Rall and Sutherland, 1958) with a suitable nonphosphate buffer. Tris-maleate buffer (20 to 80 mM) has been used in all cyclase localizations thus far, and appears to work well. The only ionic requirement for cyclase is Mg^{++} (Robison *et al.*, 1968), and concentrations as low as 4 mM are sufficient. Premature precipitation of lead in the reaction mixture can be prevented by including 7% dextran (M.W. 250,000) (Szmigielski, 1971). Since this concentration of dextran produces a viscous solution, its use in localizing cyclase in whole pieces of tissue may limit dif-

---

* Examples of enzymes capable of hydrolyzing ATP between alpha and beta phosphates are phosphoribosyl pyrophosphate amidotransferase (2.4.2.14), arginino succinate synthetase, (6.3.4.5.), and acyl-CoA synthetases (6.2.1.2.) (6.2.1.3).

fusion of substrate and other reaction media components throughout the tissue. Dextran is advantageous, however, in that it does not impart as high an osmotic pressure as does glucose or sucrose (Reik *et al.,* 1970; Howell and Whitfield, 1972). The total concentration of constituents in a reaction medium should approach isoosmolarity, which will minimize possible artifactual results of cell swelling or shrinking.

Since adenyl cyclase hydrolyzes AMP-PNP at a slower rate than it does ATP (Rodbell *et al.,* 1971), longer incubation times may be required to obtain suitable reaction product density when using this substrate. With ATP (.4 mM), reaction product is present after only 5 min of incubation at room temperature, whereas at least 25 min at the same temperature is required with AMP-PNP (.3 mM) (Wagner *et al.,* 1972). Temperature and reaction times should be regulated according to tissue characteristics and whether or not cyclase stimulators are employed.

Fixation

Fixation of liver in 1% glutaraldehyde does not completely inhibit glucagon, isoproterenol, and NaF-sensitive cyclase (Reik *et al.,* 1970), and islets of Langerhans fixed in 1% glutaraldehyde retain 20 to 40% of the glucagon and fluoride-sensitive cyclase activity of unfixed tissue (Howell and Whitfield, 1972). Capillary cyclase, however, is completely inhibited by relatively low concentrations of glutaraldehyde (0.5%) or formaldehyde (1%) (Wagner *et al.,* 1972), and isolated liver cells exhibit no cyclase activity after treatment with 0.25% glutaraldehyde (Petzold, unpublished observations). The activity of adenyl cyclase in various tissues will undoubtedly exhibit different sensitivities to fixation. However, it seems advisable to use unfixed tissue whenever possible, since unknown effects of fixation will then not intrude upon data interpretation.

Stimulators and Inhibitors

Reik *et al.* (1970) employed specific stimulators of adenyl cyclase (glucagon, isoproterenol, and NaF) to determine specificity of hormone sensitivity according to cell type in liver. The cytochemical data and biochemical measurements of cyclic AMP accumulation in the presence of these agents were also compared. The amount of precipitate observed in the presence of these stimulators was reported to roughly parallel increases in cyclic AMP accumulation in liver, and it was inferred that the observed increase in reaction product reflected the site of a stimulated enzyme.

Isolated pancreatic islets exhibit a marked increase in reaction product in the presence of 10 mM fluoride and a somewhat smaller increase after incubation in glucagon (2 μg/ml) (Howell and Whitfield, 1972). The amount of increase of reaction product observed in the presence of these agents was similar whether ATP or AMP-PNP was used as a substrate, indicating the ability of islet cyclase to hydrolyze both these compounds and also that both of the resultant products (PP_i and PNP) precipitate with lead.

A more reliable test for substrate specificity can be performed by using the specific cyclase inhibitor alloxan, which will prevent the appearance of reaction product when AMP-PNP is used as a substrate but not that formed in the presence of ATP (Wagner *et al.,* 1972). Cohn and Bitensky (1969) have shown that alloxan selectively inhibits adenyl cyclase activity in liver, brain, heart, and hamster islet cell adenomas while leaving other membrane ATPases fully active. The alloxan effects are reversible by washing, indicating that inhibition of cyclase does not result from non-specific and broad spectrum damage. The specificity of alloxan inhibition provides an additional degree of confidence in determining the enzymic source of reaction product.

Controls

If there is to be a reasonable degree of certainty that the reaction product observed demarcates a region at or near the site of cyclase activity, certain control experiments must be carried out to eliminate the possibility of artifactual precipitates. In addition to the use of specific cyclase stimulators and inhibitors to determine substrate specificity (discussed in the previous section), the following experiments can be of value in determining the source of reaction product.

(1) A substrate-free control experiment must be performed under exactly the same conditions as the experimental. Any precipitate observed under these conditions may indicate the presence of endogenous substrate in the tissue or surrounding tissues or the special affinity of some cellular constituent, other than those resulting from the hydrolysis of substrate (i.e., phosphate groups for lead), which results in the spontaneous precipitation of lead.

(2) Subjecting the tissue to high temperature (70°C) prior to incubation will denature enzymes and eliminate the possibility that reaction product is derived from the activity of other enzymes (i.e., phosphatases). Persistence of reaction product in tissue that has been treated thus may indicate spontaneous hydrolysis of substrate or nonspecific affinity for lead at a site other than that of the enzyme, causing a spontaneous precipitation of lead.

(3) The lead precipitate of a reaction product should reside in the vicinity of enzymatic activity. Theoretically, however, the products of an enzyme reaction (i.e., PNP or PP_i), once formed, may diffuse from the

site of enzyme activity and exhibit nonspecific adsorption at another cellular location. This possibility may be tested by incubating the tissue in a medium in which AMP-PNP has been replaced by PNP or ATP has been replaced by PP_i. If nonspecific adsorption is not occurring, the lead salts of PNP or PP_i will be washed out by buffer after the incubation, and no precipitate should be observed in the tissue. Observation of precipitate under these conditions, however, does not exclude the possibility that the reaction product observed in the presence of substrate is localized at the site of enzyme activity.

The diffusion of specific reaction product away from the site of catalytic activity remains a possibility in all cytochemical determinations. A gradient of precipitate away from a particular site of deposition would indicate that this is occurring. One valid control for this uncertainty is detection of cyclase activity in the specific subcellular fraction associated with that cellular structure in which the reaction product was found (i.e., plasma membranes).

SPECIFIC APPLICATIONS

Liver (Parenchymal and Reticuloendothelial Cells)

A technique for the ultrastructural localization of adenyl cyclase in liver was developed by Reik *et al.* (1970). The substrate used was ATP, and the basis for the cytochemical reaction was precipitation of the lead salt of pyrophosphate (PP_i) resulting from cyclase activity. Hormone specificity for different cell types was determined by observing variation in reaction product location in the presence of isoproterenol, glucagon, and the nonspecific stimulator, NaF. The cytochemical data and biochemical measurements of cyclic AMP accumulation in the presence of these agents were compared.

Method. (1) Rat livers previously fixed by perfusion in a solution containing 1% glutaraldehyde, 0.5 M cacodylate-nitrate buffer (pH 7.4), and 4.5% glucose were sliced (2–3 mm^3) and incubated for 30 min at 30°C in the following reaction medium:

> Tris-maleate buffer (pH 7.4) 80 mM
> Glucose 8%
> Theophylline 2mM
> $MgSO_4$ 4 mM
> ATP 0.5 mM
> $Pb(NO_3)_2$ 4.8 mM

(2) Experimental groups contained, in addition, isoproterenol (4×10^{-6} M), glucagon (1.5×10^{-7} M), and NaF (12.5×10^{-3} M).

(3) After incubation, the tissue was washed in 0.05 M Tris-maleate buffer (pH 7.4) containing 8% glucose, refixed in 1% OsO_4 in 0.05 M Veronal-acetate buffer (pH 7.4) containing 7.5% sucrose, dehydrated in ethanol and embedded in an Epon-Araldite mixture (Hayat, 1970 and 1973).

(4) Thin sections were counterstained with uranyl acetate.

(5) Biochemical measurements of cyclic AMP content (Krishna *et al.,* 1968) were made on liver incubated in the same reaction media (without $Pb(NO_3)_2$) in the presence and absence of isoproterenol, glucagon, and NaF.

Results. The reaction product formed in the presence of the two hormones exhibited a specificity according to cell type: Isoproterenol-activated cyclase was found on the external surface of parenchymal cell membranes facing the space of Disse (Fig. 6–1). Glucagon-activated cyclase was lo-

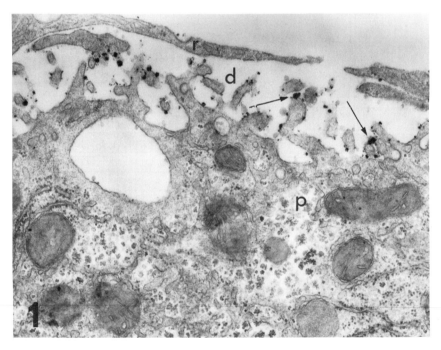

Fig. 6–1. Rat liver incubated in 0.5 mM ATP plus 4×10^{-6} M isoproterenol for 30 min at 30°C. The reaction product (arrows) is confined to the surface of the parenchymal cell (*p*) facing the space of Disse (*d*) and is absent from the reticuloendothelial cells (*r*). ×31,200.

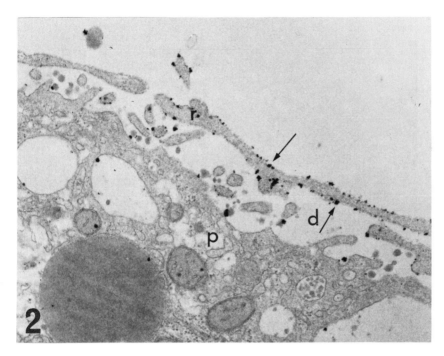

Fig. 6–2. Rat liver incubated in 0.5 mM ATP plus 1.5×10^{-7} M glucagon for 30 min at 30°C. Reaction product (arrows) is present primarily in association with reticulo-endothelial cells (r) and to a lesser extent with parenchymal cells (p). X35,000.

cated primarily on the surface of the plasma membranes of reticuloendo-thelial cells lining the hepatic sinusoids and to a lesser extent on the surface of parenchymal cells (Fig. 6–2). Reaction product was observed on both cell types in the presence of NaF, and no reaction product was found in tissue incubated without substrate, except in bile canaliculi, and this was presumed due to ATPase activity. The relative amount of precipitate in the presence of isoproterenol, glucagon, and NaF was reported to roughly parallel the degree of stimulation of cyclase activity in the presence of these agents.

These experiments indicate that different cell types in liver exhibit cy-clase activity that is hormone-specific. However, other biochemical data (Bitensky *et al.*, 1968; Sweat and Hupka, 1971) suggest that the bulk of both glucagon and isoproterenol sensitive cyclase is associated with the liver parenchymal cell. Polarization of isoproterenol-sensitive cyclase was detected on that portion of the plasma membrane of parenchymal cells facing the space of Disse.

The bile canaliculi exhibited a hormone-independent reaction product, suggesting that the product observed on the plasma membrane of parenchymal cells was hormone-dependent. Since the base levels of cyclase activity in liver are low (Bitensky *et al.,* 1968), the ability of this cyclase to be turned on by hormones with the concomitant appearance of reaction product gives credence to the supposition that the reaction product observed arises from cyclase activity. The enzymic source of the reaction product is, however, still in doubt, as lead phosphate from ATPase activity may have been a complicating factor.

Islets of Langerhans (Alpha and Beta Cells)

Cyclic AMP has been implicated in the regulation of insulin secretion from pancreatic beta cells (Mallaise *et al.,* 1967; Montague and Cook, 1971; Turtle and Kipnis, 1967) and of glucagon secretion from alpha cells (Chesney and Schofield, 1969; Leclercq-Meyer *et al.,* 1971). Adenyl cyclase has been characterized in these cells (Atkins and Matty, 1971; Davis and Lazarus, 1972), but information has not been available on the cellular location of cyclase in pancreatic islets.

Howell and Whitfield (1972) first utilized the specific cyclase substrate AMP-PNP in the cytochemical localization of cyclase in pancreatic islets. Cytochemical data were correlated with direct measurements of cyclase activity in isolated islets subjected to glucagon, NaF, and fixation with glutaraldehyde.

Method. (1) Islets of Langerhans were isolated from the pancreas of rats by the method of Howell and Taylor (1966), and were left either unfixed or fixed for 1 hr at room temperature in a solution containing 1% glutaraldehyde, 0.05 M cacodylate-nitrate buffer (pH 7.4), and 4.5% glucose.

(2) After washing and storage in the same buffer overnight at 4°C, the islets were incubated for 30 or 60 min at 30°C in the following medium:

> Tris-maleate buffer (pH 7.4)   80 mM
> Glucose   8%
> Theophylline   2 mM
> $MgSO_4$ 4 mM
> ATP   0.5 mM or AMP-PNP   0.5 mM
> Pb $(NO_3)_2$ 4 mM

(3) Experimental groups contained, in addition, either glucagon (2 μg/ml) or NaF (10 mM).

(4) After incubation, the islets were washed in Tris-maleate-glucose

buffer, refixed in 1% OsO_4 in cacodylate-nitrate buffer, dehydrated in ethanol, and embedded in epoxy resin.

(5) Thin sections were examined either without staining or after counterstaining with a saturated solution of uranyl acetate in 50% ethanol.

(6) Adenyl cyclase activity was measured directly by the method of Ramachandran (1971) by incubating the tissue in the same medium (step 2) and ATP-^{32}P. The effects of fixation, NaF, and glucagon on the enzyme activity were thus determined.

Results. Islets fixed in 1% glutaraldehyde retained 20 to 40% of the activity of unfixed tissue, and exhibited glucagon and fluoride sensitivity. It was also shown that AMP-PNP provided an effective substrate for islet cyclase, since the dilution of the specific activity of ATP-^{32}P with increasing concentrations of either AMP-PNP or ATP resulted in an almost parallel diminution of cyclic AMP-^{32}P formed.

Adenyl cyclase was localized uniformly on the outer surface of the plasma membranes of both alpha and beta cells (Fig. 6–3). No polariza-

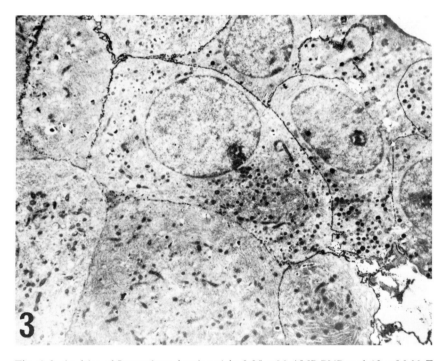

Fig. 6–3. An islet of Langerhans incubated in 0.05 mM AMP-PNP and 10 mM NaF for 30 min at 30°C. Both alpha and beta cells exhibit reaction product on the entire surface of their plasma membranes (uranyl acetate stained). ×4,100.

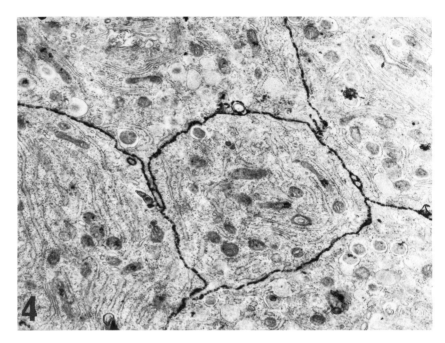

Fig. 6–4. Beta cells of an isolated rat islet incubated in 0.5 mM AMP-PNP and 10 mM NaF. Precipitate is present on the outer surface of the plasma membranes, and clearly delineates the intracellular clefts (uranyl acetate stained). ×14,700.

tion of activity was observed at the secretory pole of the cells bordering capillaries. Reaction product was seen to closely follow the invaginations of the intracellular clefts (Fig. 6–4).

NaF markedly increased the quantity of precipitate, and glucagon increased it to lesser extent in the presence of both ATP and AMP-PNP. Overall, however, the precipitate formed in the presence of AMP-PNP was less intense than that formed with ATP as a substrate. No reaction product was observed in association either with insulin secretion granules within the cytoplasm or on that portion of the plasma membrane formed by fusion of secretion granules with the cell surface. No reaction product was observed in substrate-free controls or in those islets which had been previously incubated at 70°C for 15 min.

These experiments indicate that AMP-PNP provides an effective substrate for adenyl cyclase in pancreatic islets, and that cyclase resides uniformly over the entire surface of both alpha and beta cells. Since both of these cell types were labeled in the presence of either NaF or glucagon, no specificity for hormones according to cell type can be inferred. The ability of NaF and glucagon treatment to stimulate cyclase activity and to increase the amount of reaction product formed supports the contention that the precipitate results from adenyl cyclase activity.

No polarization of cyclase activity was detectable on the cell surface. However, reaction product was absent from the membranes of insulin storage granules and from that portion of the plasma membrane derived from recently fused granules. This indicates a heterogeneity of enzymic composition between the plasma membrane and the membrane surrounding the storage granules.

Capillary Endothelial Cells

Endothelial cells line various compartments within organisms, including the entire vascular system, and are thus found embedded in all tissues. Some adenyl cyclase functions associated with vascular tissues may reside in the cells lining its blood vessels. An example of such complications arising from the cellular heterogeneity of tissues is prostaglandin-sensitive fat cyclase. Intact epididymal fat pads respond to prostaglandin E_1 with increased levels of cyclic AMP, while isolated adipocytes exhibit reduced levels of cyclic AMP in the presence of PGE_1 (Butcher and Baird, 1968). The discovery of capillary cyclase (Wagner et al., 1972) provides an intriguing explanation for this paradox.

Various phosphatase activities such as ATPase (Marchesi and Barrnett, 1963) and 5'-nucleotidase (Smith and Ryan, 1971) have been cytochemically localized in micropinocytic caveolae and vesicles which are specializations of the endothelial cell membrane involved in transcellular transport. Since cyclase utilizes ATP as a substrate, some of the reaction product associated with ATPase activity in endothelial cells may be lead pyrophosphate resulting from adenyl cyclase activity.

Wagner et al. (1972) have utilized the specific cyclase substrate AMP-PNP in localizing adenyl cyclase in a preparation of capillaries isolated from epididymal fat. The cellular homogeneity of this system reduces the possibility of diffusion of substrate or reaction product from surrounding tissue. Determinations were carried out on fresh unfixed tissue, and the effects of fixation on enzyme activity did not intrude upon data interpretation. The specific cyclase inhibitor was employed as a test for the specificity of reaction product.

Method. (1) Intact capillary networks were obtained from epididymal fat according to the method of Wagner et al. (1972) and washed in tyrodes basal salt solution (pH 7.2). They were then incubated for 5 min or 25 min at room temperature in the following reaction medium:

Tris-maleate buffer (pH 7.2)   20 mM
Dextran (M.W. 250,000)   7%
$MgSO_4$ 4 mM
Aminophylline   5 mM
ATP   0.4 mM or AMP-PNP   0.3 mM
$Pb(NO_3)_2$ 2 mM

(2) After incubation, the capillaries were washed in Tris-maleate buffer and fixed for 30 min in 2% glutaraldehyde in tyrodes-cacodylate buffer (pH 7.4).

(3) The capillaries were then pelleted in microfuge tubes in a Beckman 152 microfuge at 11,000 g. The pellets were cut out of the tubes and re-fixed in 2% OsO_4 in tyrodes-cacodylate buffer for 1 hr.

(4) The osmicated pellets were dehydrated in ethanol, and embedded in Epon (Hayat, 1972). Thin sections were observed either without staining or after counterstaining for 10 min in saturated uranyl acetate.

(5) Intracellular cyclic AMP was measured by the method of Steiner et al., (1969) and the effect of catecholamines, prostaglandins, and various other substances on cyclase activity in capillaries was determined.

Results. Capillaries incubated for 25 min with AMP-PNP exhibited reaction product primarily on the luminal surface of the endothelial cell membrane (Fig. 6–5). It appeared in patches along smooth portions of the membrane (Fig. 6–5), in most pinocytic invaginations, in vesicles free within the cytoplasm, and in intracellular junctions (Fig. 6–6). When AMP-PNP was used as a substrate, no reaction product was observed in the presence of 5 mM alloxan.

When ATP was used as a substrate, within 5 min of incubation, reaction product was observed within all micropinocytic invaginations, in free vesicles within the cytoplasm, and in intracellular junctions (Figs. 6–7 and 6–8). Alloxan was unable to inhibit the reaction product when ATP was used as a substrate.

No precipitate was observed in the substrate-free control or in capillaries which had been incubated at 70°C for 5 min prior to treatment with either ATP or AMP-PNP. When imidodiphosphate was used in place of substrate, no precipitate which would indicate nonspecific binding of reaction product was detectable.

Capillary cyclase was found to be stimulated by various catecholamines and prostaglandins but relatively nonresponsive to various other hormones and effectors (Wagner et al., 1972).

This demonstration of capillary cyclase should alert investigators to the possibility that endothelial cells may be the source of a significant fraction

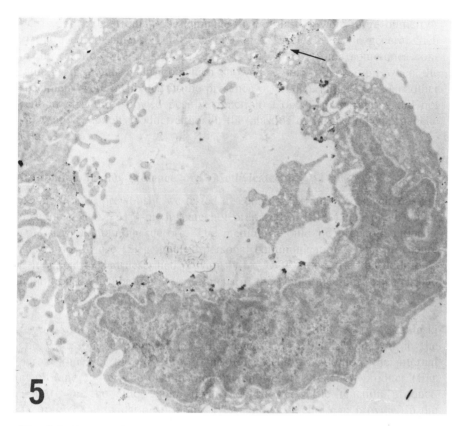

Fig. 6–5. Cross section of an isolated capillary treated with 0.3 mM AMP-PNP for 25 min at room temperature (not counterstained). Reaction product is localized in patches along smooth portions of the luminal membrane, in some micropinocytic invaginations, in vesicles free within the cytoplasm, and in intracellular junctions (arrow). X23,600.

of cyclic AMP generated by well-vascularized tissues. The association of reaction product with the luminal side of the endothelial cell membrane demonstrates a polarity of cyclase activity to that surface of the cell which first comes into contact with circulating hormones. The localization of cyclase activity in micropinocytic structures implicates cyclase with the primary function for which capillary endothelial cells are specialized. Since hormones bind to the plasma membrane prior to activating cyclase (Bitensky and Gorman, 1972), the presence of cyclase activity in micropinocytic vesicles and in intracellular junctions may provide a clue to the mechanism whereby some hormones are transported from the blood to the tissues.

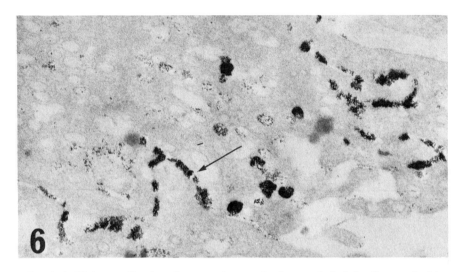

Fig. 6–6. High-magnification electron micrograph of an endothelial cell treated with 0.3 mM AMP-PNP exhibiting reaction product in intracellular junctions (arrow) and within internalized micropinocytic vesicles (not counterstained). X66,700.

Rod Outer Segments (photoreceptor membranes)

Rod outer segments prepared from the retinas of various vertebrates contain adenyl cyclase with a specific activity significantly higher than any previously recorded tissue (Bitensky *et al.,* 1971). This photoreceptor cyclase can be regulated by illumination, suggesting that cyclic AMP may participate as an intermediary in visual excitation. Homogenization of rod outer segments or treatment with digitonin results in a loss of light sensitivity of photoreceptor cyclase (Bitensky *et al.,* 1972). This suggests that the structural integrity of the disk membranes is necessary for coupling the rhodopsin to photoreceptor cyclase. Isolated disk membranes exhibit as much as 40% of the total cyclase activity in whole rod outer segments, and the predominance of cyclase activity may reside in these membranes.

Adenyl cyclase has been cytochemically localized in isolated rod outer segments by Bitensky *et al.* (1973) by employing the specific cyclase substrate AMP-PNP. Cyclase activity was found associated with the membranes of the disk lamella of the rod outer segments, and both reaction product and cyclase activity were significantly reduced in the presence of alloxan.

Method. (1) Rod outer segments were prepared from frog retinas according to the method of Bitensky *et al.* (1972), and unfixed specimens were incubated in the following medium for 25 min at room temperature:

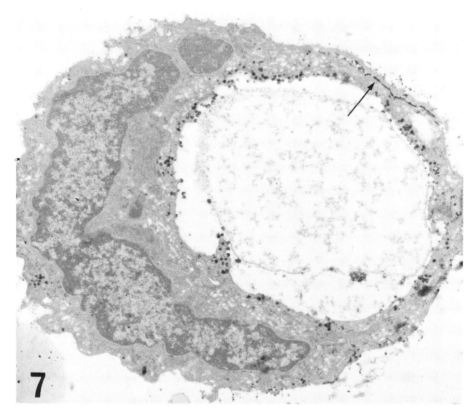

Fig. 6–7. Cross section of a capillary treated with 0.4 mM ATP for 5 min at room temperature (uranyl acetate stained). Precipitate is localized within pinocytic invaginations on the luminal and abluminal surfaces of the endothelial cell. X24,000.

Tris-maleate buffer (pH 7.2)	20 mM
Dextran (M.W. 250,000)	7%
MgSO$_4$	4 mM
Aminophylline	5 mM
AMP-PNP	0.3 mM
Pb (NO$_3$)$_2$	2 mM

(2) Control groups contained no substrate or substrate plus 5 mM alloxan.

(3) After incubation, the rod outer segments were washed in Trismaleate buffer (pH 7.2) and fixed for 60 min in 2% glutaraldehyde in tyrodes-cacodylate buffer (pH 7.4).

(4) The fixed tissue was then pelleted in microfuge tubes in a Beckman

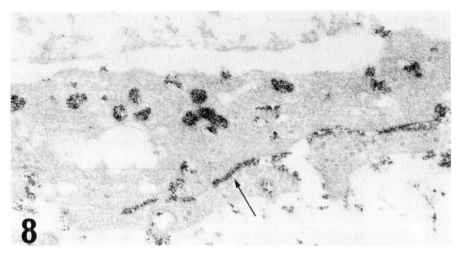

Fig. 6–8. High-magnification electron micrograph of a capillary wall treated with 0.4 mM ATP (uranyl acetate stained). Precipitate is localized within micropinocytic invaginations, in vesicles enclosed within the cytoplasm, and in intracellular junctions (arrow). ×73,300.

152 microfuge at 12,000 R.P.M. The pellets were cut out of the tubes and washed in tyrodes-cacodylate buffer.

(5) The pellets were then refixed in 2% OsO_4 in tyrodes-cacodylate buffer for 1 hr, dehydrated in ethanol, embedded in Epon, and sectioned (Hayat, 1972 and 1973).

(6) Thin sections were observed either unstained or counterstained for 10 min in saturated uranyl acetate.

Results. Rod outer segments incubated in AMP-PNP for 25 min exhibited patches of electron-dense reaction product among the lamella of the disk membranes (Fig. 6–9). Higher-magnification micrographs reveal that the product was situated on the membranes and in the spaces between the membranes (Fig. 6–10). In most cases, it was not possible to discern whether reaction product occurred on the outside or the inside surface of the disk membranes, and there was no preponderance of activity in the disk or interdisk compartments. Reaction product was absent from substrate-free controls, and 5 mM alloxan produced a significant reduction in detectable precipitate.

These experiments demonstrate the presence of cyclase in an intracellular membrane system. Whether this cyclase system remains coupled to light-sensitive rhodopsin was not discernible with this technique.

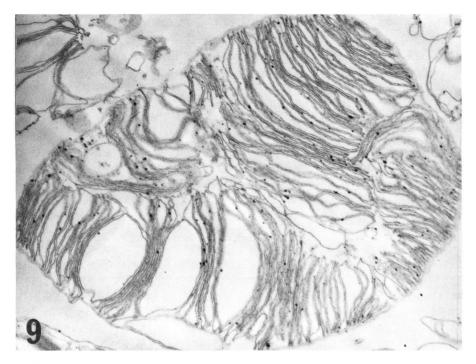

Fig. 6–9. An isolated rod outer segment incubated for 25 min at room temperature in 0.3 mM AMP-PNP (not counterstained). Small patches of reaction product are present in association with the lamella of the disk membranes. X31,700.

CONCLUDING REMARKS

Various cytochemical procedures have permitted ultrastructural localization of adenyl cyclase previously unattainable by standard biochemical techniques. Specific hormone sensitivity of cyclase according to cell type has been demonstrated in liver (Reik *et al.*, 1970). Cyclase activity is polarized to that portion of the plasma membranes of liver parenchymal cells facing the space of Disse (Reik *et al.*, 1970) and on the luminal surface of endothelial cells lining the capillaries (Wagner *et al.*, 1972).

The membranes surrounding insulin storage granules in pancreatic beta cells are devoid of cyclase activity, as are those areas of the plasma membrane formed by fusion of the granules with the cell surface (Howell and Whitfield, 1972). This indicates a heterogeneity of enzymic composition between the plasma and storage granule membrane. Discrete discontinuity of cyclase activity is also evident on the plasma membrane of capillary endothelial cells (Wagner *et al.*, 1972). The relatively high cyclase ac-

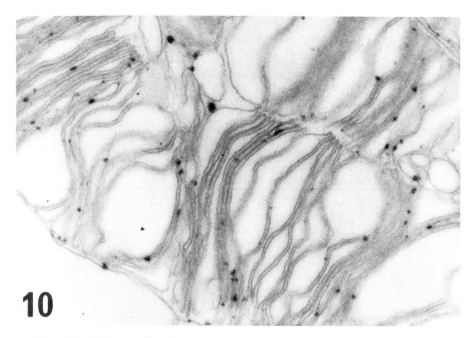

Fig. 6–10. High-magnification electron micrograph of a portion of an isolated rod outer segment incubated in 0.3 mM AMP-PNP (not counterstained). Reaction product on the surface of the disk membranes. ×58,500.

tivity of photoreceptor outer segments has localized on the membranes of the intracellular disk lamellae (Bitensky *et al.,* 1973).

The specific cyclase substrate AMP-PNP which will not be hydrolyzed by other membrane ATPases is useful in determining the enzymic source of reaction product. Further studies are required to rule out the possibility that other soluble enzymes which can utilize AMP-PNP are the source of some of the reaction product. However, the use of this substrate in conjunction with various cyclase stimulators and the specific cyclase inhibitor alloxan combine to form an effective cytochemical probe for adenyl cyclase.

REFERENCES

Atkins, T., and Matty, A. J. (1971). Adenyl cyclase and phosphodiesterase activity in the isolated islets of Langerhans of obese mice and their lean litters. *J. Endocrin.* **51,** 67.

Bitensky, M. W., and Gorman, R. E. (1973). Cellular responses to cyclic AMP. In: *Recent Progress in Biophysics and Biochemistry.* Pergamon Press Ltd. Oxford, England (in press).

Bitensky, M. W., Gorman, R. E., and Miller, W. H. (1971). Adenyl cyclase as a link between photon capture and changes in membrane permeability of frog photoreceptors. *Proc. Nat. Acad. Sci.* **68,** 561.

Bitensky, M. W., Gorman, R. E., and Miller, W. H. (1972). Digitonin effects on photoreceptor cyclase. *Science* **175,** 1363.

Bitensky, M. W., Keirns, J. J., and Wagner, R. C. (1973). Cyclic AMP and photoreceptor function. In: *Biochemistry and Physiology of Visual Pigments* (Baumann, C., Bonting, S. L., Hamdorf, K. and Langer, H., eds.). Springer-Verlag, Berlin and New York (in press).

Bitensky, M. W., Russell, V., and Robertson, W. (1968). Evidence for separate epinephrine and glucagon responsive adenyl cyclase systems in rat liver. *Biochem. Biophys. Res. Comm.* **31** (5), 706.

Butcher, R. W., and Baird, C. E. (1968). Effects of prostaglandins on adenosine 3′-5′-monophosphate levels in fat and other tissues. *J. Biol. Chem.* **243,** 1713.

Butcher, R. W., Robison, G. A., and Sutherland, E. W. (1972). Cyclic AMP and hormone action. In: *Biochemical Actions of Hormones* (Litwack, G., ed.). Academic Press, New York and London.

Butcher, R. W., and Sutherland, E. W. (1962). Adenosine 3′-5′-phosphate in biological materials. I. Purification and properties of cyclic 3′-5′-nucleotide phosphodiesterase and the use of this enzyme to characterize adenosine 3′-5′-phosphate in human urine. *J. Biol. Chem.* **237,** 1244.

Chesney, T. M., and Schofield, J. G. (1969). Studies on the secretion of pancreatic glucagon. *Diabetes* **18,** 627.

Cohn, K. L., and Bitensky, M. W. (1969). Inhibitory effects of alloxan on mammalian adenyl cyclase. *J. Pharm. Exp. Therapeutics* **169,** (1) 80.

Davis, B., and Lazarus, N. R. (1972). Insulin release from mouse islets: Effect of glucose and hormones on adenyl cyclase. *Biochem. J.* **129,** 373.

Davoren, R. R., and Sutherland, E. W. (1963). The cellular location of adenyl cyclase in the pigeon erythrocyte. *J. Biol. Chem.* **238,** 3016.

Essner, E. (1973). Phosphatases. In: *Electron Microscopy of Enzymes: Principles and Methods,* Vol. 1 (Hayat, M. A., ed.). Van Nostrand Reinhold Company, New York and London.

Hayat, M. A. (1970). *Principles and Techniques of Electron Microscopy: Biological Applications, Vol. 1.* Van Nostrand Reinhold Company, New York and London.

Hayat, M. A. (1972). *Basic Electron Microscopy Techniques.* Van Nostrand Reinhold Company, New York and London.

Hayat, M. A. (1973). Specimen preparation. In: *Electron Microscopy of Enzymes: Principles and Methods,* Vol. 1 (Hayat, M. A., ed.). Van Nostrand Reinhold Company, New York and London.

Howell, S. L., and Taylor, A. (1966). Effects of glucose on incorporation of ^{3}H leucine into insulin in isolated rabbit islets of Langerhans. *Biochem. Biophys. Acta* **130,** 519.

Howell, S. L., and Whitfield, M. (1972). Localization of adenyl cyclase in islet cells. *J. Histochem. Cytochem.* **20** (11), 873.

Jost, J. P., and Rickenberg, A. V. (1971). Cyclic AMP. *Ann. Rev. Biochem.* **40,** 741.

Krishna, G., Harwood, J. P., Barber, A. J., and Jamieson, G. A. (1972). Requirement for guanosine triphosphate in the prostaglandin activation of adenylate cyclase of platelet membranes. *J. Biol. Chem.* **247** (7), 2253.

Krishna, G., Weiss, B., and Brodie, B. B. (1968). A simple sensitive method for the assay of adenyl cyclase. *J. Pharm. Exp. Therapeutics* **163**, 379.

Leclerq-Meyer, V., Brisson, G. R., and Malaisse, W. J. (1971). Effect of adrenalin and glucose on the release of glucagon and insulin in vitro. *Nature* (London) **231**, 248.

Malaisse, W. J., Malaise-Lagae, F., and Mayhew, D. (1967). A possible role for the adenyl cyclase system in insulin secretion. *J. Clin. Invest.* **46**, 1724.

Marchesi, V. T., and Barrnett, R. J. (1963). The demonstration of enzymatic activity in pinocytic vesicles of blood capillaries with the electron microscope. *J. Cell Biol.* **17**, 547.

Montague, W., and Cook, H. R. (1971). The role of 3'-5'-cyclic monophosphate in the regulation of insulin release by isolated rat islets of Langerhans. *Biochem. J.* **122**, 115.

Pohl, S. L., Birnbaumer, L., and Rodbell, M. (1969). Glucagon-sensitive adenyl cyclase in the plasma membrane of the hepatic parenchymal cell. *Science* **164**, 566.

Rall, T. W., and Sutherland, E. W. (1958). Formation of a cyclic adenine ribonucleotide by tissue particles. *J. Biol. Chem.* **232**, 1065.

Ramachandran, J. (1971). A new simple method for separation of adenosine 3'-5'-cyclic monophosphate from other nucleotides and its use in the assay of adenyl cyclase. *Ann. Biochem.* **43**, 227.

Reik, L., Petzold, G. L., Higgins, J. A., Greengard, P., and Barnett, J. (1970). Hormone-sensitive adenyl cyclase: Cytochemical localization in rat liver. *Science* **168**, 382.

Robison, G. A., Butcher, R. W., and Sutherland, E. W. (1968). Cyclic AMP. *Ann. Rev. Biochem.* **37**, 149.

Rodbell, M., Birnbaumer, L., Pohl, S. L., and Kranz, H. M. (1971). The glucagon-sensitive adenyl cyclase system in plasma membranes of rat liver. V. An obligatory role of guanyl nucleotides in glucagon action. *J. Biol. Chem.* **246** (6), 1877.

Smith, U., and Ryan, J. W. (1971). Pinocytic vesicles of the pulmonary endothelial cell. *Chest* **59** (5) (suppl.), 12s.

Steiner, A. L., Kipnis, D. M., Utiger, R., and Parker, C. (1969). Radioimmunoassay for the measurement of adenosine 3'-5'-cyclic phosphate. *Proc. Nat. Acad. Sci.* **64**, 367.

Sutherland, E. W., and Rall, T. W. (1958). Fractionation and characterization of a cyclic adenine ribonucleotide formed by tissue particles. *J. Biol. Chem.* **232**, 1077.

Sutherland, E. W., Robison, G. A., and Butcher, R. W. (1968). Some aspects of the biological role of adenosine 3'-5'-monophosphate (cyclic AMP). *Circulation* **37**, 279.

Sweat, F. W., and Hupka, A. (1971). Adenyl cyclase in hepatic parenchymal and reticuloendothelial cells. *Biochem. Biophys. Res. Comm.* **44**, 1436.

Szmigielski, S. (1971). The use of dextran in phophatase techniques employing lead salts. *J. Histochem. Cytochem.* **19**, 505.

Turtle, J. R., and Kipnis, D. M. (1967). An adrenergic receptor mechanism for the control of cyclic 3'-5'-adenosine monophosphate synthesis in tissues. *Biochem. Biophys. Res. Comm.* **28**, 797.

Wachstein, M., and Meisel, E. (1957). Histochemistry of hepatic phosphatases at a physiological pH with special reference to the demonstration of bile canaliculi. *Amer. J. Clin. Path.* **27**, 13.

Wagner, R. C., Kriener, P., Barrnett, R. J., and Bitensky, M. W. (1972). Biochemical characterization and cytochemical localization of a catecholamine-sensitive adenylate cyclase in isolated capillary endothelium. *Proc. Nat. Acad. Sci.* **69** (11), 3175.

Yount, R. G., Babcock, D., Ballentyne, W., and Ohala, D. (1971). Adenylylimidodiphosphate: An adenosine triphosphate analog containing a P-N-P linkage. *Biochemistry* **10,** 2484.

7

Lipase

TETSUJI NAGATA

*Department of Anatomy, Shinshu University School of Medicine,
Matsumoto, Japan*

INTRODUCTION

Lipase was first named by Hanriot (1896), who found this enzyme in the serum and tissues which hydrolyze monobutyrin. According to the nomenclature of the International Enzyme Commission (1961), lipase (E.C. 3.1.1.3) is called by its systemic name, glycerol-ester-hydrolase, which belongs to the hydrolases. However, for the sake of convenience, the name lipase will be used in this chapter.

Lipase can be included with the esterases, which are often divided into three groups: nonspecific esterases, lipase, and cholinesterases. Nonspecific esterases hydrolyze alcohol esters of short-chain fatty acids; lipase hydrolyzes glycerol esters of long-chain fatty acids; and cholinesterases hydrolyze cholin and acetylcholin, which are esters of alcohols containing nitrogen. According to Lake (1972a and b), the differentiation of lipases from esterases based on the chain length of the fatty acid ester is not valid. He has suggested that esterase and lipase be referred to as fatty acid ester hydrolase. Seligman (1972), on the other hand, has emphasized the differences in the properties of these two enzymes. It has been demonstrated that cholate (Kramer *et al.,* 1964) and taurocholate (Nachlas and Seligman, 1949) are activators of lipase and inhibitors of esterase. Such observations are evident in tissues, tissue homogenates, and sera. There is no doubt that esterase does hydrolyze short-chain fatty acid esters preferentially, and that lipase hydrolyzes long-chain fatty acid esters preferentially. The esterases will be dealt in detail by Shnitka in Volumes 3 and 4 of this series.

Biochemical evidence for the presence of lipases in the serum and tissues (e.g., pancreas, liver, and stomach) of various animals has long been available. The histochemical demonstration of its presence was first presented by Gomori (1945). The histochemical principle that was employed had earlier been used for the localization of phosphatase activity. Since then, many studies have been carried out to localize this enzyme (Wachstein, 1946; Gomori, 1948; Mark, 1950; Sneath, 1950; Stowell and Lee, 1950; Kurata and Hoso, 1951; Richterich, 1952; Martin, 1953; Takeuchi et al., 1953; Takeuchi and Furuta, 1956; George and Iype, 1959 and 1960; Abe et al., 1964; Bokdawala and George, 1964; Takkar et al., 1969).

Using Tween 40 as a substrate, Mizuhira and Kurotaki (1962) reported the ultrastructural localization of lipase in liver cells. Although they reported the deposition of lead-containing reaction product in the mitochondria, no electron micrographs were published. Since they did not specify the concentration of the lead nitrate solution, it is assumed that no attention was paid to this aspect of the procedure. Nonspecific lead deposition is therefore inevitable; this point will be discussed later.

Seligman et al. (1966) reported a new technique for the demonstration of lipase at both the light and electron microscope levels. Their technique is based upon the formation of osmiophilic diazothioethers by S-coupling fast blue BBN with the hydrolysis product, mercaptobenzanilide. This is followed by exposure to osmium tetroxide vapors, which results in the formation of osmium blacks. This technique is based on a method introduced by Kramer et al. (1963) for localizing lipase at the light microscope level. In this method, naphthol-AS nonanoate was used as a substrate, and sodium taurocholate as an activator. Kramer et al. (1963), after comparing the rates of hydrolysis of a series of naphthyl alkanoates, found that nonanoic acid ester of naphthol-AS was preferentially hydrolyzed by pancreatic lipase in the presence of bile salts.

However, the blue azo dye did not possess sufficient electron opacity and was lipid soluble, so that extraction occurred during the dehydration and embedding of specimens. Therefore this procedure could not be used in cytochemistry. These disadvantages were overcome by Hanker et al. (1964 and 1966) by using the reducing properties of thiolesters to react with osmium tetroxide vapors. This reaction results in the formation of electron-opaque osmium black product, which is insoluble in solvents used in tissue preparatory procedures. Seligman *et al.* (1966) further developed this principle to form diazothioethers from 2-thiolnonanoylbenzanilide in dimethylacetamide and diazonium salt (Fast blue BBN), which was converted to electron-opaque black product after exposure to osmium tetroxide vapors.

The above procedure seems complicated, and results in large osmium black deposits which are not ideal for precise localization of lipase activity. Murata *et al.* (1968) and Nagata and Murata (1972) developed a modified technique of lead precipitation based upon Gomori's original method for light microscopy. This technique is simpler, and the staining results are consistent. Fine lead precipitates are formed which permit a precise localization of lipase activity.

FIXATION

Tissue specimens are initially fixed in 2.5 to 5.0% glutaraldehyde buffered with 0.1 M cacodylate (pH 7.2) for 1 hr at 4°C. Although 1 hr fixation causes some inhibition of enzymic activity, a longer duration will result in a drastic inhibition. The cacodylate buffer can be stored in a refrigerator for several months. The glutaraldehyde solution should be prepared immediately prior to use. The final fixative is prepared as below:

0.1 M *Cacodylate buffer* (pH 7.2)

Sodium cacodylate	2.14 gm
Distilled water	100 ml (total)
0.1 M HCl solution	8.4 ml

Glutaraldehyde solution

25% glutaraldehyde (highly purified)	1 ml
0.1 M cacodylate buffer	9 ml

Fresh tissue slices (1 mm³) or frozen sections are fixed by immersion and washed in three changes of the buffer for 5 min each.

INCUBATION

Preparation of Tissues

By using a freezing microtome, the fixed and washed tissue slices are cut into 50 μ thick sections. This is accomplished by placing several slices on the freezing stage along with a few drops of the buffer, and the temperature is set at −20°C. The freezing is completed when the upper part of the tissue slice appears pale white and firm. This requires usually only a few minutes. The temperature is maintained at $-20°C$ for a few more minutes while the upper part of the slices begins to thaw. A number of sections are cut with the microtome knife. If the sections adhere to the knife, remove the individual sections after each stroke by using a camel's hair brush and suspend them in the buffer in a Petri dish.

According to Blanchette-Mackie (personal communication), the freezing microtome can produce a mechanical displacement of cellular components, particularly in lipid-laden tissues. The lipid droplets in these tissues are not fixed by glutaraldehyde, and a "smearing" effect occurs with the freezing microtome. Thus, as a check for the effects of the freezing microtome, small tissue blocks (less than 1 mm³) should be rapidly hand-cut before fixation. These blocks can be treated in the same manner as the freezing microtome sections. The outer surface of these blocks, perhaps 10 μ in depth, should subsequently be examined with the electron microscope. In some tissues, the localization of reaction product is different in the freezing microtome sections from the localization in blocks of tissue. These methods should be compared for each type of tissue.

Composition of the Incubation Media

Gomori's Original Medium

0.2 M Tris (hydroxymethyl) aminomethane buffer (pH 7.2 to 7.4)	5.0 ml
10% aqueous calcium chloride solution	2.0 ml
5% Tween 80 (or 60) solution	2.0 ml
Distilled water	40.0 ml

This author has used various modifications of Gomori's medium, and they are listed below:

Incubation Medium A

5% Tween 80 solution	1.0 ml
0.2 M Tris buffer (pH 7.2)	2.5 ml
10% aqueous calcium chloride	1.0 ml
Distilled water	20.5 ml

Incubation Medium B

5% Tween 80 solution	1.0 ml
0.2 M Tris buffer (pH 7.2)	2.5 ml
10% aqueous calcium chloride	1.0 ml
2.5% aqueous sodium taurocholate	2.5 ml
Distilled water	18.0 ml

Incubation Medium C

5% Tween 80 solution	1.0 ml
0.2 M Tris buffer (pH 7.2)	2.5 ml
0.08 to 0.02% aqueous lead nitrate solution	1.0 ml
Distilled water	20.5 ml

Incubation Medium D

0.2 M Tris buffer (pH 7.2)	2.5 ml
10% aqueous calcium chloride	1.0 ml
Distilled water	21.5 ml

Incubation Medium E

5% Tween 80 solution	1.0 ml
0.2 M Tris buffer (pH 7.2)	2.5 ml
10% aqueous calcium chloride	1.0 ml
Quinine hydrochloride	0.099 gm
Distilled water	20.5 ml

Preincubation Medium F

0.2 M Tris buffer (pH 7.2)	2.5 ml
Distilled water	22.5 ml
Sodium fluoride	0.21 gm

Distilled water used in preparing solutions should be boiled for 5 min to remove carbon dioxide. Either Tween 60 or Tween 80 can be used as the substrate. We prefer Tween 80 because it is an unsaturated fatty acid (oleic acid) ester, which is a liquid and can be measured with a pipette. 0.5 ml of Tween 80 is dissolved in 9.5 ml distilled water, which can be stored in a refrigerator for several weeks. 0.2 M Tris aminomethane maleate buffer (pH 7.2) is prepared as follows:

29 gm of maleic acid and 30.3 gm of Tris (hydroxymethyl) aminomethane are dissolved in 500 ml distilled water. After adding 2 gm activated charcoal, the solution is shaken for 10 min and filtered. To 40 ml of this solution, add 20 ml of 1 N NaOH and make up to 100 ml with distilled water.

Substrates

The substrates used by Gomori were Tween 20 (lauryl acid ester), Tween 40 (palmitic acid ester), Tween 60 (stearic acid ester), and Tween 80 (oleic acid ester). Tween 20, Tween 40, and Tween 60 are saturated fatty acid esters, while the Tween 80 is an unsaturated fatty acid ester. Using chick embryo and Gomori's method, Buno and Marino (1952) demonstrated that Tween 80 localizes not only lipase but also nonspecific esterases. Yoshimura (1955) showed that Tween 80 was decomposed by nonspecific esterases.

In order to differentiate between lipase and nonspecific esterases, Takeuchi et al. (1953) improved the method by staining the end product of calcium with Nile blue for light microscopy. However, studies of Tween 60 and Tween 80 by Nagata and Murata (1972) indicated no difference between the two substrates. The specificity of the substrates will be discussed later.

Incubation Temperature

The best results are obtained when the incubation is carried out at 37°C; the use of a water bath is recommended.

Duration of Incubation

Satisfactory reaction products can be obtained by employing a duration of 1 to 18 hr. The reaction products are found in the endoplasmic reticulum, perinuclear space, Golgi apparatus, secretory canaliculi, glandular lumina (Fig. 7–1), and membranes of zymogen granules (Fig. 7–2). The size of the reaction product varies, depending upon the duration of incubation. An 18-hr incubation resulted in deposits of reaction product of 200 to 300 μ in length, and 100–150 μ in width, and almost cylindrical in shape within the endoplasmic reticulum (Fig. 7–3). These deposits are restricted to the cisternae of endoplasmic reticulum.

The deposits appear as irregular spheres having diameters of 100 to 150 μ after 3-hr incubation (Fig. 7–4). The reaction products seem not to leak out from the lipase-active sites as long as the duration of incubation ranges from 1 to 18 hr. The size of the reaction products, however, increases as the duration of incubation is increased. Longer durations of incubation cause the reaction to be more obvious, while shorter durations are useful for obtaining precise localization of the enzyme activity.

SUBSTITUTION WITH LEAD SOLUTION

Routine Procedure

Tissue specimens incubated in medium A, B, D, or E are washed in 2% EDTA in cacodylate buffer (pH 7.2) for 3 min to remove calcium (Adams et al., 1966). This solution is prepared by dissolving 2 gm EDTA in 100

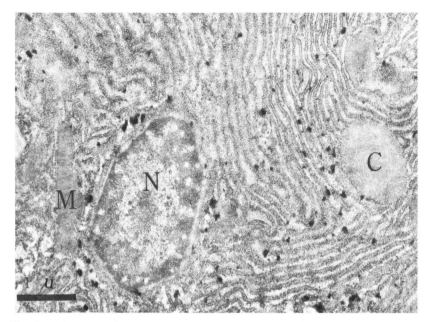

Fig. 7–1. A pancreatic acinar cell of a normal mouse after incubation in medium B containing Tween 80 for 3 hr and substituted with 0.25% lead nitrate solution. Lead deposits are seen in the cisternae of rough endoplasmic reticulum, but not in the nucleus (N), mitochondria (M), and crystalloid (C).

ml cacodylate buffer. The specimens are washed in the buffer and then immersed in 0.15% aqueous lead nitrate solution for 10 min at room temperature in order to substitute calcium. This solution is prepared by dissolving 0.15 gm lead nitrate in 100 ml distilled water which has been boiled for 5 min to remove carbon dioxide.

One-Step Procedure

The routine procedure consists of two steps. In the first step, calcium ions are used as the capture reagent; in the second step, the reaction products of the first step is substituted with lead ions. In the one-step method, lead ions are used directly as the capture reagent as given in the medium C. Although the one-step method has been employed successfully to localize lipoprotein lipase activity (Blanchette-Mackie and Scow, 1971), we have not been successful in localizing lipase activity by using this method. Moreover, Blanchette-Mackie has indicated that when lead ions are used alone as the captive reagent, the enzyme activity is reduced. On the other hand, the one-step method has proved successful in localizing alkaline phosphatase by using lead ions (Mölbert *et al.,* 1960) or cadmium ions (Mizutani

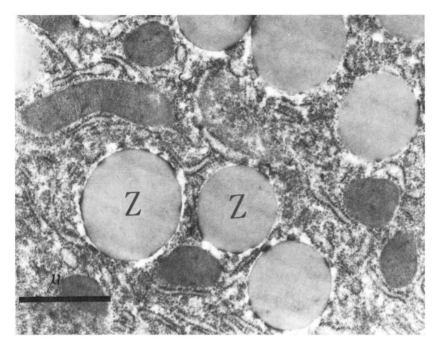

Fig. 7–2. A pancreatic acinar cell of a normal mouse fixed with 5% glutaraldehyde, incubated in medium A, and substituted with 0.1% lead nitrate solution. Note that lead deposits are limited to the membranes of zymogen granules (Z); mitochondria and rough endoplasmic reticulum do not show any deposits.

and Barrnett, 1965). The reasons for the difference in the ability of the one-step method to localize lipase activity and alkaline phosphatase are not known, and need to be elucidated.

It is pointed out that when the tissue is exposed to lead prior to enzyme-substrate interaction, the results may be a rapid inhibition of the enzyme activity. On the other hand, when the enzyme and the substrate are com-plexed prior to adding lead, the enzyme should become more resistant to "degradation" by lead ions.

POSTFIXATION

After the tissue specimens have been immersed in the lead nitrate solution, they are washed with 0.1 M cacodylate buffer for 5 min and then postfixed with buffered osmium tetroxide for 1 hr at 0°C. The specimens are dehy-drated rapidly according to the method by Hayat (1972 and 1973) and embedded in Epon according to standard procedures. Sections are post-stained with uranyl acetate followed by lead citrate.

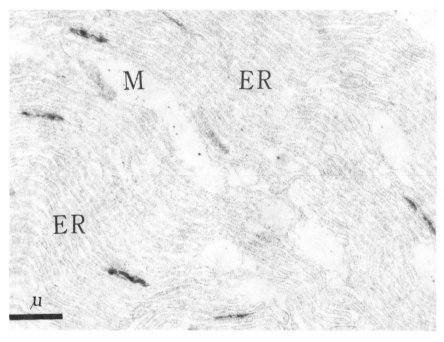

Fig. 7–3. A pancreatic acinar cell of a normal mouse fixed with 2.5% glutaraldehyde, incubated in medium B containing Tween 60 for 18 hr, and substituted with 0.15% lead nitrate solution. Cylindrical-shaped lead deposits are limited to rough endoplasmic reticulum (*ER*); mitochondria (*M*) do not show any deposits.

RESULTS

Tissue specimens incubated in medium A or B and substituted with lead nitrate solutions having concentrations above 0.5% or washed in sucrose solution prior to the lead treatment showed nonspecific lead depositions throughout the cytoplasm and the nucleus. Such nonspecific deposits were observed also in the specimens incubated in the medium without the substrate or in the medium D. The best results were obtained by using 0.15% lead nitrate solution.

DISTRIBUTION

The pancreatic tissues incubated in medium A and substituted with 0.15% lead nitrate solution showed reaction products limited to the membranes of zymogen granules and in the glandular lumen of acinar cells. On the

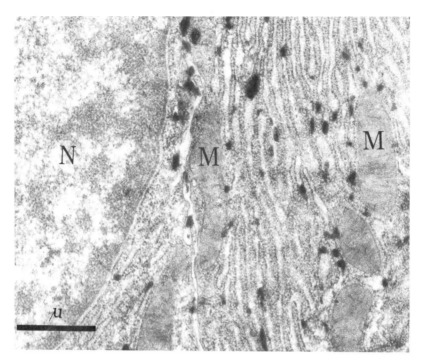

Fig. 7–4. A pancreatic acinar cell of a normal mouse fixed with 5% glutaraldehyde, incubated in medium B containing Tween 80 for 3 hr, and substituted with 0.15% lead nitrate solution. Irregular ellipsoidal lead deposits are seen in the cisternae of rough endoplasmic reticulum; nucleus (N) and mitochondria (M) do not show any deposits.

other hand, the specimens incubated in medium B and substituted with 0.15% lead nitrate solution showed reaction products in the cisternae of endoplasmic reticulum and Golgi apparatus, perinuclear space, and membranes of zymogen granules. Plasma membrane, microvilli, and acinar lumen showed reaction products, as also reported by Murata *et al.* (1968). Some reaction products were present around the inclusion bodies, as also reported by Nagata *et al.* (1968).

The specimens incubated in media C and D did not show any lead deposits. The specimens incubated in medium E containing quinine hydrochloride or preincubated in medium F followed by incubation in media A and B also did not show any deposits. The specimens incubated in medium A or B followed by fixation, without substitution with lead nitrate solution, did not show any deposits. These results indicate that the best media are A and B. It can also be concluded that the lipase which is synthesized in the cisternae of endoplasmic reticulum is transferred to the Golgi apparatus, then to the periphery of the zymogen granules, and finally discharged into the acinar lumen.

The above results also indicate that the zymogen granules and the glandular lumen showed positive reaction with both media A and B, whereas the cisternae of endoplasmic reticulum, Golgi apparatus, and perinuclear space showed positive reaction with medium B but not with medium A. It is inferred that the lipase found in the zymogen granules and the glandular lumen is the active type, while the enzyme found in the cisternae of endoplasmic reticulum, Golgi apparatus, and perinuclear space is the inactive type. This inactive type lipase is activated by sodium tauro-cholate present in medium B. The fact that lipase activity is found only in the zymogen granules with medium A accords well with the biochemical results obtained by Arnesjo and Grubb (1969) with cell fractionation. They showed that the lipase activity was found only in the zymogen gran-ules and plasma membrane fractions.

SPECIFICITY OF THE REACTION

The specificity of the lead precipitation method for lipase should be con-sidered in terms of the roles played by the inhibitors and accelerators, differentiation of lipase from nonspecific esterases, and nonspecific lead depositions.

Nonspecific Lead Depositions

As described in the results, the use of sucrose solutions and the concen-tration of lead nitrate solutions are the two primary parameters affecting the lead deposition. The pH of the latter solutions can also affect non-specific lead deposition. The size and shape of the lead soaps can vary, depending upon the pH of the lead solution used to precipitate them.

Sucrose Solutions

When sucrose solutions are used, before or after the incubation, nonspecific lead deposits are formed throughout the karyoplasm and cytoplasm. These deposits are called metallophilia. Similar deposits have been reported while demonstrating acid phosphatase activity (Ogawa *et al.,* 1962). Therefore the use of sucrose solutions cannot be recommended.

Concentration of Lead Nitrate Solution

The concentration of lead nitrate solution is probably the most important factor that affects the nonspecific lead depositions. When the concentration exceeds 0.5%, nonspecific deposition is common; when it is kept below 0.25%, the deposits are mostly specific. Lead nitrate solutions with a concentration range of 0.1 to 0.15% are recommended.

Differentiation from Nonspecific Esterases

The differentiation of lipase reaction from that of nonspecific esterases can be accomplished by utilizing the substrate specificity, the inhibitors, and the accelerators. The ideal substrates for lipase were supposed to be the glycerides of long-chain fatty acids; for esterases, the simple esters of short-chain carboxylic acids. However, a considerable degree of overlapping in enzymatic hydrolysis by these two classes of enzymes occurs, since both can split esters of fatty acids of intermediate chain length.

Nachlas and Seligman (1949) have compared esterolytic activities of the pancreas, liver, and kidney by using three chromogenic substrates of different size chains prepared from beta-naphthol and fatty acids and beta-naphthol esters of acetic acid (C_2), and lauric acid (C_{12}) and palmitic-stearic acid (C_{16-18}). They found that the pancreas, which contained esterase and lipase, hydrolyzed all three substrates; and that the liver and kidney, which contained only esterases, hydrolyzed only acetate and laurate. It was concluded that the most important differentiating factor is the length of the fatty acid molecule chain.

In other words, lipase acts most efficiently upon esters of long-chain fatty acids, while esterases act upon esters of short-chain fatty acids; the glycerol component does not seem to play any determinative role. Therefore, in order to demonstrate lipase activity in pancreas, various kinds of Tweens (which are esters of long-chain fatty acids) can be used. However, it has been indicated that the lipase activity in rat gastric mucosa increased against the hydrolysis of triglyceride trioctanoin (which has a medium-sized chain) when the animals were fed with olive oil (Barrowman and Darnton, 1970). These results suggest the importance of the organ in determining the substrate specificity.

The Tweens commonly used at the light microscope level have been mentioned earlier. Gomori (1945) first suggested that the reaction products with Tween 80 demonstrated the sites of true lipase activity. However, it was later pointed out by Gomori (1948 and 1949) and others (Nachlas and Seligman, 1948 and 1949) that the differentiation of true lipase from nonspecific esterases was not easy. The identification cannot be wholly determined from the kind of substrate used. Although Diaconita (1965) reported that the incubation medium with Tween 60 at pH 7.4 did not distinguish lipase from esterase in the guinea pig lung, he recommended the incubation medium with Tween 80 at pH 8.5 for lipase localization. Nagata and Murata (1972), however, found no significant difference between the reactions of Tween 60 and Tween 80 even at the subcellular level.

In accordance with the development of azo-coupling methods for the localization of nonspecific esterases at the light microscope level, azo coupling in combination with inhibitors and accelerators has been widely used for identifying specific esterases from nonspecific esterases. On the other hand, the lead precipitation method has not been widely used (Deane et al., 1960). This method causes a slight diffusion of enzyme activity, and requires a relatively long duration of incubation because of the slow penetration of the substrate Tween into the tissue specimens. On these and other grounds, Pearse (1961) discouraged the use of this method. Nevertheless, this author maintains that the lead precipitation method, when combined with appropriate inhibitors and accelerators, can be employed for differentiating lipase reaction from that of nonspecific esterases.

Inhibitors and Accelerators

It is important to employ the inhibitory action of various reagents to differentiate specific esterase reaction from that of nonspecific esterases. The inhibitory effect of certain reagents specifically upon the lipase activity in the pancreas was first pointed out by Rona and Pavlovic (1922). This biochemical study dealt with quinine and atoxyl. Gomori (1948) histochemically examined the effect of eleven inhibitors on the Tween method, and found that the esterase activity was inhibited by quinine (5×10^{-4} M), arsenilate (2×10^{-4} M), and taurocholate (0.02 M). Taurocholate was found to activate the lipase activity in pancreatic acinar cells. Gomori and Chessick (1953) demonstrated that di-iso-propylfluorophosphate (DFP, 10^{-6} M) completely inhibited the color reaction of Tween method, while fluoride (2×10^{-3} M) had no effect.

Nachlas and Seligman (1949) found that: eserine (3.5×10^{-3} M) inhibited both the lipase and esterase activity; sodium arsenilate (10^{-1} M) and fluoride (3 mg/cc) inhibited only esterase activity; quinine hydrochloride (10^{-2} M) inhibited only lipase activity; and sodium taurocholate (10^{-2} M) accelerated lipase and slightly inhibited esterase activity. Myers and Mendel (1953) found that esterases were inhibited by atoxyl (10^{-2} M) and phosphate derivatives, while lipase was not affected. Myers et al. (1955) found that organo-phosphorous derivatives such as E 600, DIMP, and DFP inhibited esterases, whereas lipase was not affected. Spannhof and Kreutzmann (1969) examined E 600 and trichlorphone (10^{-5} M) with carbonic acid esters of naphthol AS derivatives, and found that esterases were inhibited, whereas lipase remained unaffected.

The media given above were prepared keeping in mind the above-mentioned results. The negative and positive reactions obtained with these media confirmed the usefulness of specific inhibitors and accelerators in localizing lipase activity.

SUMMARY

The standard procedure for localizing lipase activity in animal tissues is summarized below:

(1) Small tissue blocks are fixed with 2.5% glutaraldehyde buffered with 0.1 M cacodylate buffer (pH 7.2) for 1 hr at 0 to 4°C.

(2) The specimens are washed in 0.1 M cacodylate buffer, three changes, for 5 min each.

(3) Approximately 50 μ thick frozen sections are cut with a freeze microtome at −20°C.

(4) The sections are incubated in the five media listed above for 3 hr at 37°C.

(5) The sections are treated with 2% EDTA in cacodylate buffer (pH 7.2) for 5 min.

(6) The sections are washed on 0.1 M cacodylate buffer for 5 min.

(7) The sections are immersed in 0.15% lead nitrate solution for 10 min.

(8) The sections are washed in 0.1 M cacodylate buffer for 5 min.

(9) The sections are postfixed with 1% osmium tetroxide in 0.1 M cacodylate buffer for 1 hr.

(10) The sections are washed in the buffer for 10 min.

(11) The sections are dehydrated in graded series of acetone and embedded in Epon.

(12) Ultrathin sections are poststained with uranyl acetate followed by lead citrate.

REFERENCES

Abe, M., Kramer, S. P., and Seligman, A. M. (1964). The histochemical demonstration of pancreatic-like lipase and comparison with the distribution of esterase. *J. Histochem. Cytochem.* **12**, 364.

Adams, C. W. M., Abdulia, Y. H., Bayliss, O. B., and Weller, R. O. (1966). Histochemical detection of triglyceride esters with specific lipases and a calcium-lead sulphide technique. *J. Histochem. Cytochem.* **14**, 385.

Arnesjo, B., and Grubb, A. (1969). Intracellular distribution of lipase in comparison to trypsinogen, amylase, and immediately measurable trypsin inhibitors in the rat pancreas. *Acta Physiol. Scand.* **75**, 139.

Barrowman, J. A., and Darnton, S. J. (1970). The lipase of rat gastric mucosa: A histochemical demonstration of the enzymatic activity against a medium chain tryglyceride. *Gastroenterology* **59**, 13.

Blanchette-Mackie, E. J., and Scow, R. O. (1971). Sites of lipoprotein lipase activity in adipose tissue perfused with chylomicrons. *J. Cell Biol.* **51,** 1.

Block, M. A., Wakin, K. G., and Baggenstoss, A. H. (1954). Experimental studies concerning factors in the pathogenesis of acute pancreatitis. *Surg. Gynec. Obstet.* **99,** 83.

Bokdawala, F. D., and George, J. C. (1964). Histochemical demonstration of muscle lipase. *J. Histochem. Cytochem.* **12,** 768.

Buno, W., and Marino, R. G. (1952). Location of lipase activity in the chick embryo. *Acta Anat.* **16,** 85.

Commission on Enzymes of the International Union of Biochemistry (1961). *Report of the Commission on Enzymes of the International Union of Biochemistry.* Pergamon Press, London.

Deane, H. W., Barrnett, R. J., and Seligman, A. M. (1960). *Histochemische Methoden zum Nachweis der Enzymaktivität. Handbuch der Histochemie,* herausgegeben von Graumann, W., und Neumann, K. Band VII, Erster Teil: 99. Gustav Fischer Verlag, Stuttgart.

Diaconita, G. (1965). Untersuchungen über die Anwendung von Tween-Substraten für die Bestimmung der Lipaseaktivität. *Acta Histochem.* **20,** 82.

George, J. C., and Iype, P. T. (1959). A study of the lipase activity in the developing chick heart. *J. Exp. Zool.* **141,** 291.

George, J. C., and Iype, P. T. (1960). Improved histochemical demonstration of lipase activity. *Stain Technol.* **35,** 151.

Gomori, G. (1945). The microtechnical demonstration of sites of lipase activity. *Proc. Soc. Exp. Biol. Med.* **58,** 362.

Gomori, G. (1948). Histochemical differentiation between esterases. *Proc. Soc. Exp. Biol. Med.* **67,** 4.

Gomori, G. (1949). Histochemical localization of true lipase. *Proc. Soc. Exp. Biol. Med.* **72,** 697.

Gomori, G., and Chessick, R. D. (1953). Histochemical studies of the inhibition of esterases. *J. Cell Comp. Physiol.* **41,** 51.

Hanker, J. S., Seaman, A. R., Weiss, L. P., Ueno, H., Bergman, R. A., and Seligman, A. M. (1964). Osmiophilic reagents: New cytochemical principle for light and electron microscopy. *Science* **146,** 1039.

Hanker, J. S., Katzoff, L., Rosen. H. R., Seligman, M. L., and Seligman, A. M. (1966). Design and synthesis of thiolesters for the histochemical demonstration of esterase and lipase via the formation of osmiophilic diazothioethers. *J. Med. Chem.* **9,** 288.

Hanriot, M. (1896). Sur un nouveau ferment du sang. *Compt. Rend. Soc. Biol.* **48,** 925.

Hayat, M. A. (1972). *Basic Electron Microscopy Techniques.* Van Nostrand Reinhold Company, New York and London.

Hayat, M. A. (1973). Specimen preparation. In: *Electron Microscopy of Enzymes: Principles and Methods,* Vol. 1 (Hayat, M. A., ed.). Van Nostrand Reinhold Company, New York and London.

Kramer, S. P., Aronson, L. D., Rosenfeld, M. G., Sulkin, M. D., Chang, A., and Seligman, A. M. (1963). Human pancreatic lipase study with bile salt activation and substrates from a homologous series of naphthyl alkanoates. *Arch. Biochem. Biophys.* **102,** 1.

Kramer, S. P., Bartalos, M., Karpa, J. N., Mindel, J. S., Chang, A., and Seligman, A. M. (1964). Development of a clinically useful colorimetric method for serum lipase. *J. Surg. Res.* **4,** 23.

Kurata, Y., and Hoso, M. (1951). A new histochemical method for the demonstration of lipase (in Japanese) *Med. Biol.* (Tokyo) **18**, 103.

Lake, B. D. (1972a). Is the histochemical demonstration of lipase activity possible? *Histochem. J.* **4**, 71.

Lake, B. D. (1972b). When is a lipase not a lipase? *Histochem. J.* **4**, 562.

Mark, D. D. (1950). Distribution of lipase in preneoplastic and neoplastic states induced in the rat liver by paradimethylaminoazobenzene. *Arch. Pathol.* **49**, 545.

Martin, B. F. (1953). Lipase in gland duct epithelium and in mucus-secreting cells. *Nature* **172**, 1048.

Mizuhira, V., and Kurotaki, A. (1962). Electron microscopic demonstration of lipase in the liver with Tween 40 (abstract in Japanese). *Niigata Med. J.* **76**, 651.

Mizutani, A., and Barrnett, R. J. (1965). Fine structural demonstration of phosphatase activity at pH 9. *Nature* **206**, 1001.

Mölbert, E. R. G., Duspiva, F., and von Deimling, O. H. (1960). Die histochemische Lokalisation der Phosphatase in der Tubulusepithelzelle der Mäuseniere im Elektronenmikroskopischen Bild. *Histochemie* **2**, 5.

Murata, F., Yokota, S., and Nagata, T. (1968). Electron microscopic demonstration of lipase in the pancreatic acinar cells of mice. *Histochemie* **13**, 215.

Myers, D. K., and Mendel, B. (1953). Studies on ali-esterases and other lipid-hydrolysing enzymes. I. Inhibition of the esterases and acetoacetate production of liver. *Biochem. J.* **53**, 16.

Myers, D. K., Schotte, A., Boer, H., and Borsje-Bakker, H. (1955), Studies on ali-esterases and other lipid-hydrolysing enzymes: Inhibition of the esterases of pancreas. *Biochem. J.* **61**, 521.

Nachlas, M. M., and Seligman, A. M. (1949). Evidence for the specificity of esterase and lipase by the use of three chromogenic substrates. *J. Biol. Chem.* **181**, 343.

Nagata, T., and Murata, F. (1972). Supplemental studies on the method for electron microscopic demonstration of lipase in the pancreatic acinar cells of mice and rats. *Histochemie* **29**, 8.

Nagata, T., Murata, F., and Yokota, S. (1968). On the lipase activity in the crystalloids in the pancreatic acinar cells of the mouse. *Med. J. Shinshu Univ.* **13**, 23.

Ogawa, K., Shinonaga, Y., and Suzuki, T. (1962). Metallophilia of the striated border of the rat jejunal epithelial cells. *Acta Anat. Nippon.* **37**, 134.

Pearse, A. G. E. (1961). *Histochemistry, Theoretical and Applied,* 2d ed., pp. 472–75. Churchill Ltd., London.

Richterich, R. (1952). Zur Technik des histochemischen Esterasenachweises. *Acta Anat.* **14**, 263.

Rona, P., and Pavlovic, R. (1922). Über die Wirkung des Chinins und des Atoxyls auf Pankreaslipase. *Biochem. Z.* **134**, 108.

Sabatani, D., Bensch, K., and Barrnett, R. J. (1963). Cytochemistry and electron microscopy. *J. Cell Biol.* **17**, 19.

Sabatini, D. D., Bensch, K., and Barrnett, R. J. (1963). Cytochemistry and electron microscopy. The preservation of cellular structure and enzymatic activity by aldehyde fixation. *J. Cell Biol.* **17**, 19.

Seligman, A. M. (1972). Concerning overlapping activities of related hydrolases and their inconvenience to scientific study. *Histochem. J.* **4**, 561.

Seligman, M. L., Ueno, H., Hanker, J. S., Kramer, S. P., Wasserkrug, H., and Seligman, A. M. (1966). Cytochemical localization of pancreatic lipase with light and electron microscopy. *Exp. Mol. Pathol. Suppl.* **3,** 21.

Sneath, P. H. A. (1950). Histochemical demonstration of lipase. *Nature* **166,** 699.

Spannhof, L., and Kreutzmann, H. L. (1969). Zur Verwendug von Napthol AS Carbonsäure Estern zum Histochemischen Nachweis von Esterasen und Lipasen. *Acta Histochem.* **33,** 394.

Stowell, R. E., and Lee, C. S. (1950). Histochemical studies of mouse liver after single feeding of carbon tetrachloride. *Arch. Pathol.* **50,** 519.

Takeuchi, T., and Furuta, M. (1956). A modification of the dyeing method for histochemical demonstration of tissue lipase. *Kumamoto Med. J.* **9,** 70.

Takeuchi, T., Furuta, M., and Yoshimura, K. (1953). Supplement to histochemical demonstration of tissue lipase (in Japanese). *Tokyo Med. J.* **70,** 319.

Takkar, G. L., Kambou, V. P., and Kar, A. B. (1969). Effect of altered hormonal states on the histochemical distribution of lipase activity in the rat prostatic complex. *Histochemie* **20,** 21.

Wachstein, M. (1946). Influence of experimental kidney damage on histochemically demonstrable activity in the rat: Comparison with alkaline phosphatase activity. *J. Exp. Med.* **85,** 25.

Yoshimura, K. (1955). Histochemical studies on lipase. *Kumamoto Med. J.* **29,** 618.

Author Index

Subject Index

Acid phosphatase, 9, 22, 43, 142
Alkylsulfatases, 90
Artifact, 7–9, 22, 23, 38, 99, 113, 114
AT, 7, 11, 12, 14–18

BAXD, 3, 5, 10, 20
BED, 3, 5, 10
Benzidine, 1, 2, 15, 20, 21
Blood, 3, 22, 123
Brain, 17, 92, 96, 114
Buffer, 5, 6, 8, 16, 20, 24, 36, 39–41, 44–46, 51, 52, 56, 57, 69, 70, 75, 81, 82, 94–98, 101, 103, 112, 115, 116, 118, 119, 122, 125, 126, 134–139, 145

Cadmium, 36, 44, 45, 49, 50, 138
Catalase, 2, 6–11, 13, 19, 22, 24, 25, 69, 81
Catechol, 68, 69
Chloroplasts, 20, 67, 70, 73, 75, 76
Cholate, 132
Choline sulfatases, 90
Chondrosulfatases, 90, 105

Cupric ferrocyanide, 3
Cytochrome, 1, 6, 7, 10, 16–20, 22–25, 80

DAB. *See* 3-3′-Diaminobenzidine
DDC, 69, 70, 73, 81
Dehydration, 5, 35, 36, 38, 45, 46
Dehydrogenases, 3
DFP, 42
3-3′-Diaminobenzidine (DAB), 2–7, 9–14, 16–21, 23–25, 68, 69, 81
o-Dianisidine, 2
Diazonium, 94, 134
Diffusion, 2, 7–9, 22, 38, 98, 112, 114, 121, 144
o-Diphenols, 67–69
DMSO, 94, 95
DOPA, 10, 11, 67–70, 72, 73, 75–77, 79–85, 87

EDTA, 92, 137, 145
Embedding, 5, 35, 38, 45, 46
Endolpasmic reticulum, 2, 4, 5, 8–10, 12,

157